BRAIN GAMES FOR BRAIN POWER

MORE THAN 250 WORD GAMES, LOGIC PUZZLES, NUMBER CHALLENGES, AND TRIVIA QUIZZES

TRUSTED MEDIA BRANDS

New York / Montreal

Note to Readers
The consultants, writers, editors, and proofreaders have taken all reasonable measures
to confirm and verify the accuracy of the information contained in this title. However,
some statements of fact can be open to interpretation. Similarly, new information and
research often reveal that long-held beliefs are not true. We welcome your input on
any answers for which you have sound evidence may be incorrect.

STAY SHARP, STAY YOUNG

The puzzles in this book may help you improve a variety of brain skills, including your ability to remember. As the brain ages, vocabulary may remain strong, but the ability to spot meanings and search for the word you are looking for slows down.

Language puzzles exercise circuits that can help lessen forgetful moments and shorten their duration, but learning cannot become memory without concentration, and without regular maintenance, concentration shrinks with age. These puzzles provide many opportunities for improving and strengthening this important ability and many other useful brain skills:

• Pattern and pathfinding puzzles will strengthen your powers of concentration in the same way that physical exercises build aerobic stamina;

• Logic and memory puzzles will challenge your working memory because you must keep some variables in mind while you test them against others—this frontal-lobe skill is crucial to productive thinking and requires fierce concentration;

• Visual and mechanical puzzles will stretch your visual-spatial mental muscles, which you need to navigate the physical world successfully;

• Divergent-thinking puzzles will encourage your ability to think "outside the box" and see links where others see standard differences—an ability that pays off in any profession;

• Puzzles involving calculation are important to try—even if you are not a numbers person—for they light up many different parts of the brain at once.

Descriptions of the major puzzle types appear on the following pages. The games start on page 8. Good luck!

About the Puzzles

Brain Games for Brain Power is filled with a delightful mix of classic and new puzzle types. To help you get started, here are instructions, tips, and some examples.

WORD GAMES

CROSSWORD PUZZLES

Clues are the deciding factor that determine crossword-solving difficulty. Many solvers mistakenly think strange and unusual words are what make a puzzle challenging. In reality, crossword constructors generally try to avoid grid esoterica, opting for familiar words and expressions.

WORD SUDOKU

The basic sudoku puzzle is a 9 x 9 square grid, split into nine square regions, each containing nine cells. You need to complete the grid so that each row, each column, and each 3 x 3 frame contains the nine letters from the black box above the grid.

There is always a hidden nine-letter word in the diagonal from top left to bottom right.

EXAMPLE   **SOLUTION**

WORD POWER

These multiple-choice quizzes test your knowledge of grammar and language and help you develop a better vocabulary. Find out where you stand on the Word Power scale by using the simple rating system included on the answer pages.

WORD SEARCHES

In a word search, the challenge is to find hidden words within a grid of letters. Words can be found in vertical columns or horizontal rows or along diagonals, with the letters of the words running either forward or backward.

NUMBER GAMES

SUDOKU

The basic sudoku puzzle is a 9 x 9 square grid, split into nine square regions, each containing nine cells. Complete the grid so that each row, each column, and each 3 x 3 frame contains every number from 1 to 9.

EXAMPLE   **SOLUTION**

In addition to classic sudoku puzzles, you'll find **SUDOKU X** puzzles, where the main diagonals must include every number from 1 to 9, and **SUDOKU TWINS,** with two overlapping grids.

KAKURO

These puzzles are like crosswords with numbers. There are clues across and down, but the clues are numbers. The solution is a sum that adds up to the clue number.

Each number in a black area is the sum of the numbers that you have to enter in the next empty boxes. The empty boxes that make up the sum are called a run. The sum of the across run is written above the diagonal in the black area, while the sum of the down run is written below the diagonal.

Runs must contain only the numbers 1 through 9, and each number in a run can be used only once. The gray boxes contain only odd numbers; the white contain only even numbers.

EXAMPLE   **SOLUTION**

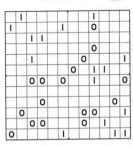

LOGIC PUZZLES

BINAIRO

Binairo puzzles look similar to sudoku puzzles. They are just as simple and challenging, but that is where the similarity ends.

There are two versions: odd and even. The even puzzles feature a 12 x 12 grid. You need to complete the grid with zeros and ones, until there are 6 zeros and 6 ones in every row and every column. No more than two of the same number can be next to or under each other. Rows or columns with exactly the same combination are not allowed.

EXAMPLE   **SOLUTION**

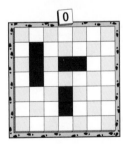

The odd puzzles feature an 11 x 11 grid. You need to complete the grid with zeros and ones until there are 5 zeros and 6 ones in every row and column.

KEEP GOING

In this puzzle, start on a blank square of your choice and connect as many blank squares as possible with one single continuous line.

You can only connect squares along vertical and horizontal lines, not along diagonals. You must continue the connecting line up until the next obstacle—i.e., the rim of the box, a black square, or a square that has already been used.

You can change direction at any obstacle you meet. Each square can be used only once. The number of blank squares left unused is marked in the upper square. There may be more than one solution, but we include only one solution in our answer key.

EXAMPLE   **SOLUTION**

About the Puzzles *(continued)*

NUMBER CLUSTER

Number cluster puzzles are language-free, logical numerical problems. They consist of cubes on a 6 x 6 grid. Numbers have been placed in some of the cubes, while the rest are empty. Your challenge is to complete the grid by creating runs of the same number and length as the number supplied. So where a cube with the number 5 has been included on the grid, you need to create a run of five number 5's, including the cube already shown. The run can be horizontal, vertical, or both horizontal and vertical.

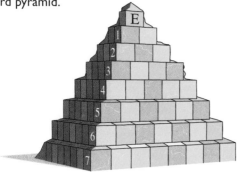

EXAMPLE   SOLUTION

WORD PYRAMID

Each word in the pyramid has the letters of the word above it, plus a new letter.

Using the clues given, answer No.1 and then work your way to the base of the pyramid to complete the word pyramid.

SPORT MAZE

This puzzle is presented on a 6 x 6 grid. Your starting point is indicated by a red cell with a ball and a number. Your objective is to draw the shortest route from the ball to the goal, the only square without a number. You can move only along vertical and horizontal lines, but not along diagonals. The figure on each square indicates the number of squares the ball must be moved in the same direction. You can change direction at each stop.

EXAMPLE   SOLUTION

CAGE THE ANIMALS

This puzzle presents you with a zoo divided into a 16 x 16 grid. The different animals on the grid need to be separated. Draw lines that will completely divide up the grid into smaller squares, with exactly one animal per square.

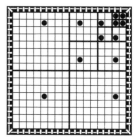

EXAMPLE   SOLUTION

TRIVIA

TRIVIA QUIZZES & TRIVIAL PURSUITS

Trivia in a variety of formats and topics will probe the depth of your knowledge of facts. Questions and answers will tempt, tease, and tickle.

VISUAL PUZZLES

Throughout you will find unique mazes, visual conundrums, and other colorful challenges. Each comes with a new name and unique instructions. Our best advice? Patience and perseverance. Your eyes will need time to unravel the visual secrets.

BRAINSNACK® PUZZLES

To solve a BrainSnack® puzzle, you must think logically. You'll need to use one or several strategies to detect direction, differences, and/or similarities, associations, calculations, order, spatial insight, colors, quantities, and distances. A BrainSnack® ensures that all the brain's capacities are fully engaged. These are brain sports at their best!

FIND THE RIGHT WORD

Can you find a word within this grid? Arrows are scattered on the grid. Each arrow points toward a letter that is part of the solution word, but the letters cannot be next to each other vertically, horizontally, or diagonally.

M		←	↙		E		↙
→		L	→				O
					D		
R	↓						↙
			A			↑	M
	A				↑		

BRAINTEASERS

You'll also find short brainteasers scattered throughout these pages. These puzzles will provide some light relief from the more intense puzzles while still challenging you.

Trophy Room

ACROSS

1 NFL aerial
5 Roomer's board
10 "Be that ___ may ..."
14 Have a common border
15 Razzle-dazzle
16 Dog's best friend?
17 In the neighborhood
18 Treasure chest
19 Club for McIlroy
20 Tennis trophy
22 Glove interior
24 Singer Franklin
25 Butcher's cut
26 Charley-horse area
28 Like the Tower of London, supposedly
31 Speed of sound
34 Handbill
36 Prefix for blast
37 "___ Follow the Sun": Beatles
38 It can be bent or lent
39 Chapel Hill college
40 Be a front-runner
42 Keeps bar
44 Figure heads?
45 Makes bubbly
47 Oscar Night presenter
49 Rubbernecker
50 The Last Frontier
54 Bird dog
56 Soccer trophy
58 Stephen King's St. Bernard
59 ___-garde
61 Anderson of "WKRP"
62 "Make ___ for it!"
63 She turned men into swine
64 Sundance's Place
65 Old Rome wear
66 Finalized
67 *South Park* kid

DOWN

1 Jack Black's ursine role
2 "Fuzzy Wuzzy was ___ ..."
3 Debonair
4 Elaine in *Autumn in New York*
5 Laurie in *Making Mr. Right*
6 Fabric shade
7 Crooked
8 Washroom, informally
9 Sidereal
10 Mindless
11 NASCAR trophy
12 Babe Ruth, e.g.
13 Zesty flavor
21 "___-La-La": Shirelles
23 Marker
27 Takes to the woods
28 Chisholm Trail sights
29 Sicilian spouter
30 Savage and Holliday
31 Kunis in *Ted*
32 To the protected side
33 Golf trophy
35 Holm in *Time Bandits*
41 "500" city
42 Sunbathing spot
43 Didn't begin on the bench
44 Holds protectively
46 Woodstock shirt
48 In toto
51 Aussie golfer Adam
52 Kinte of *Roots*
53 Like royal jelly
54 Sing like Cleo Laine
55 Coin of the Continent
56 Rachel in *The Thorn Birds*
57 "___ in Love with Amy"
60 Diesel in *Saving Private Ryan*

BRAINSNACK® **Play the Slots**

Below the wheels of the slot machine, you see a wheel laid out flat.
Which symbol (1–6) should replace the question mark?

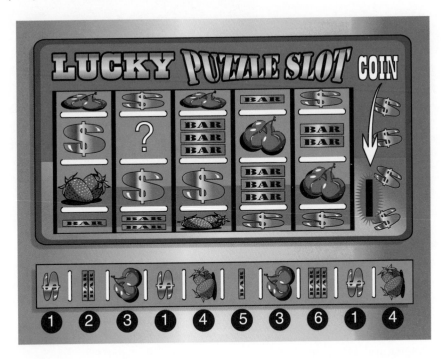

CLOCKWISE

The answers to the clues from 1 to 12 are all seven-letter
words that end with the letter N. When you have solved
the puzzle correctly, working clockwise from 1, the 12
letters in the outer circle will spell a word a nosy person.

1 The Orient
2 Skilled craftsperson
3 Deer
4 Wearing away
5 Crocus-derived spice
6 Manner of enunciation

7 Repeated phrase
8 A formal speech
9 Large water bird
10 Model person
11 Made of baked clay
12 A boundary, crossed by Caesar

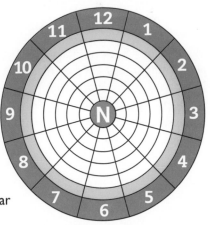

The Christmas Movie

Christmas comes only once a year, but the questions about
Christmas movies can be asked year-round!

1. Who played *Scrooge* in the 1988 film
Scrooged?

   a. John Belushi
   b. Will Farrell
   c. Bill Murray

2. Who played Santa in the 1994 film
Miracle on 34th Street?

   a. Richard Dreyfuss
   b. Richard Attenborough
   c. Billy Crystal

3. In which 1946 film did James Stewart
attempt to commit suicide at Christmas?

   a. *It's a Wonderful Life*
   b. *The Philadelphia Story*
   c. *Harvey*

4. Which Bond film features Dr. Christmas
Jones?

   a. *Dr. No*
   b. *Moonraker*
   c. *The World Is Not Enough*

5. Which film sees Arnold Schwarzenegger
attempting to buy a Turbo Man doll for
his son's Christmas present?

   a. *The Santa Claus*
   b. *Bad Santa*
   c. *Jingle All the Way*

6. Who played Scrooge in *The Muppet
Christmas Carol?*

   a. Michael Caine
   b. Steve Martin
   c. Tim Curry

7. In which 1998 film does Michael Keaton
play a deceased father who comes back
to life as a snowman?

   a. *Desperate Measures*
   b. *Jack Frost*
   c. *The Paper*

8. The 1982 animated film *The Snowman*
featured which boy soprano singing
"Walking in the Air"?

   a. Yves Abel
   b. Peter Auty
   c. Aled Jones

9. Which wrestler played the title role in
the 1996 film *Santa with Muscles?*

   a. Hulk Hogan
   b. Mickey Rourke
   c. Rocky Johnson

10. Who played Mr. Lawrence in the 1983
film *Merry Christmas, Mr. Lawrence?*

    a. Tom Hanks
    b. Tom Cruise
    c. Tom Conti

WORD SEARCH · House

All the words are hidden vertically, horizontally, or diagonally—in both directions. The letters that remain unused form a sentence from left to right.

```
S T U D I O L B A T H R O O M
C A N H O L L O W W A L L A T
P O T I E C L D A E T S D E B
E A L W I N D O W S I L L B C
T S N O I T A D N U O F D E H
S D E R N G U T T E R I I D I
R R O H C N A L L A W R S R M
O F F I C E A R C A D E A O N
O C R E T T I D A R A E S O E
D O C T A E B L E G L S T M Y
E R L A D R D E I R E C O T H
A R T I S R I N S N T A V A K
O I T A P U L L E D G P E C I
N D S I T T I N G A R E A T O
T O W O D N I W R E M R O D H
D R A I N P I P E E T F L O O
N E H C T I K R O A F A N A T
T R O O L F I S H U T T E R C
```

- ARCADE
- BATHROOM
- BEDROOM
- BEDSTEAD
- CEILING
- CHIMNEY
- COLONNADE
- CORRIDOR
- DOORSTEP
- DORMER WINDOW
- DRAINPIPE
- FIRE ESCAPE
- FLOOR
- FOUNDATIONS
- GARAGE
- GUTTER
- HAT RACK
- HOLLOW WALL
- KITCHEN
- OFFICE
- PATIO
- SHUTTER
- SITTING AREA
- STOVE
- STUDIO
- TURRET
- WALL ANCHOR
- WELL
- WINDOWSILL

Themeless 1

ACROSS

1 Reddish-yellow pear
5 Campus newbie
10 Call at a base
14 *Malcolm in the Middle* ranch owner
15 Paperboy's area
16 Odd, in Oban
17 *Way Out West* costar
19 Corn Belt city
20 Kind of contract
21 Convenience
23 Apprehend
24 Combines
25 Former Russian first lady
27 Proven sound
30 Drift, as an aroma
33 Disney duck princess
35 Ballet's Shearer
36 Slugger's stat
37 Blue
39 Year in Trajan's reign
40 Goof
42 Someone special
43 Department with ties
44 Dale Earnhardt, Jr.'s org.
46 InDesign company
48 Convictions
50 Xylophone striker
54 *Brothers & Sisters* star
56 Run a machine
57 Wall or buck ender
58 Sign of contractions
60 Chipper
61 Kidney-related
62 Envisioned
63 1040 IDs
64 Toots
65 *For Better or For Worse* mom

DOWN

1 ___ nova
2 Bewhiskered fish-eater
3 "You're Sixteen" singer
4 Proselytize
5 Small part
6 Libertine
7 For us
8 Commandment verb
9 Cycling accessory
10 Stinker
11 Cease-fire
12 Express worry
13 Comparable to pie?
18 One of the Simpsons
22 Adversary
24 Bunched fruits
26 Artsy Manhattan area
28 ___ go Bragh!
29 Roasting spot?
30 Small songbird
31 Charm opener
32 Heir to a throne, typically
34 Copied
37 Sky: Comb. form
38 Without further ado
41 Rainforest cats
43 Hollywood district
45 Bonus
47 Boxer in *Cinderella Man*
49 Comanche shelter
51 Corsage spot
52 Merman in *Gypsy*
53 Diminutive
54 Emulates Drake
55 Azurite and tinstone
56 Glacial ridges
59 Homer's "___ Lee Shore"

Cards at the Table

In the looking-glass spirit, the following Kings, Queens, and Jacks are having tea. However, their seating etiquette is very complicated, and the four rules below must be followed: Can you work out who must sit where? To help you, one card is already in place.

1. No one of the same suit may sit opposite or next to each other.
2. The Kings must have equal status.
3. Queens without their Kings must sit between a King and his Queen.
4. The Queen of Diamonds has asked to sit on the King of Clubs' left (she's his sister!).

Keep Going

Start on a blank square of your choice and connect as many blank squares as possible with one single continuous line. You can only connect squares along vertical and horizontal lines, not along diagonal lines. You must continue the connecting lineup until the next obstacle, i.e., the border of the box, a black square, or a square that already has been used. You can change direction at any obstacle you meet. Each square can only be used once. The number of blank squares that will be left unused is marked in the upper square. There is more than one solution. We only show one solution.

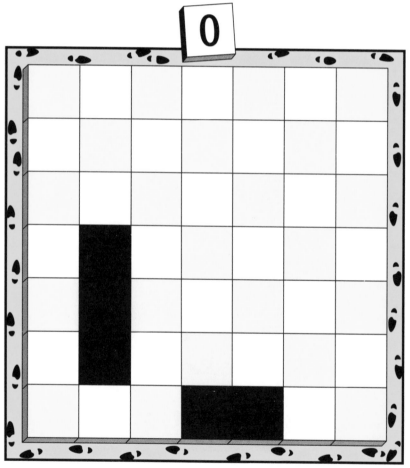

delete ONE

Delete one letter from

MANLY AS IF FATE

and rearrange the rest to let your imagination run wild.

14

WORD POWER Time

While the basics—morning, noon, evening—suffice just fine,
this quiz highlights the many ways we can indicate time. Test your knowledge,
then see the light of day with the answers.

· ·

1. **per diem** (per 'dee-em) *adv.*—
   A: daily. B: twice a day.
   C: every other day.

2. **noctambulist** (nok-'tam-byoo-
   list) *n.*— A: early riser.
   B: sleepwalker.
   C: one who fears the moon.

3. **fortnight** ('fort-niyt) *n.*—
   A: wee hours. B: two weeks.
   C: holiday's eve.

4. **soiree** (swah-'ray) *n.*—
   A: high tea. B: birthday.
   C: evening party.

5. **circadian** (sir-'kay-dee-en)
   adv.—A: in sunlight.
   B: in insect season.
   C: in 24-hour cycles.

6. **ides** ('iydz) *n.*—A: odd hours.
   B: mid-month days.
   C: omens at night.

7. **adjourn** (uh-'jurn) *v.*—
   A: wake up. B: exercise.
   C: call it a day.

8. **curfew** ('ker-fyoo) *n.*—
   A: dog day. B: short nap.
   C: restriction at night.

9. **reveille** ('reh-vuh-lee) *n.*—
   A: hour-long drill.
   B: wake-up call.
   C: noon break.

10. **crepuscular** (kre-'pus-kyuh-ler)
    adv.—A: at twilight.
    B: of holy hours.
    C: of morning dew.

11. **repast** (ree-'past) *n.*—
    A: prior day.
    B: anniversary.
    C: time of a meal.

12. **contemporary** (kuhn-'tem-puh-
    rer-ee) *adv.*—A: part-time.
    B: tomorrow.
    C: present-day.

13. **du jour** (doo 'zhur) *adv.*—
    A: just for today.
    B: within the hour.
    C: of legal holidays.

14. **swing shift** ('swing shift) *n.*—
    A: 4 p.m. to midnight.
    B: midnight to dawn.
    C: 9 a.m. to 5 p.m.

15. **advent** ('ad-vent) *n.*—
    A: commercial holiday. B: day off.
    C: coming or arrival.

Sport Maze

Draw the shortest way from the ball to the goal. You can only move along vertical and horizontal lines, not along diagonal lines. The figure on each square indicates the number of squares the ball must move in the same direction. You can change direction at each stop.

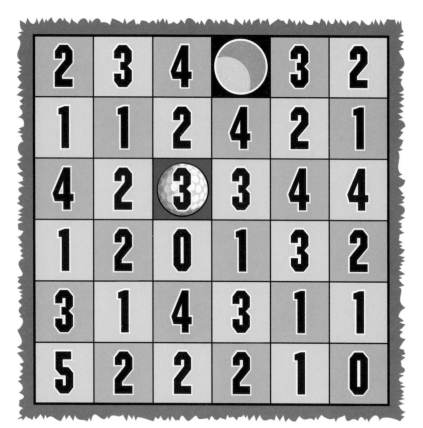

ONE LETTER LESS OR MORE

The word on the right side contains the letters of the word on the left side, plus or minus the letter in the middle. One letter is already in the right place.

| A | N | T | I | P | O | D | E | -I | | | T | | | |

CROSSWORD ▸ **Tic-Tac-Toe Winners**

ACROSS

1 Carved gem
5 Granite, once
10 "Ain't She Sweet?" composer
14 *Exodus* author
15 *Lou Grant* star
16 Pained expression
17 000
19 *For a Few Dollars* ___ (1966)
20 Holy smoke
21 Paint spray
23 Wise goddess
24 Hydra head count
25 ___ *fide* (in bad faith)
27 *The English* ___ (1996)
30 The worst
33 Smithy tool
35 *The Morning Watch* novelist
36 Old English letter
37 Indian bean dish
38 Hood's heater
39 Strap attached to a bridle
41 Roundup
43 ___ of Man
44 Esai of *Vanished*
46 Having originated in
48 Scott in the 1857 news
49 New York fruits
53 Abbott and Costello film
56 What opposites do
57 A, to pilots
58 XXX
60 Ensuing
61 Chekov of *Star Trek*
62 Saltimbocca meat
63 Bait fish
64 Clear the slate
65 East, in Madrid

DOWN

1 Roberts in *Mirror Mirror*
2 "___ You Glad": Beach Boys
3 Moat
4 Regards highly
5 Fortified wine of Sicily
6 U.S. Open stadium name
7 Striped antelope
8 Prefix with bucks or bytes
9 Ammo depot
10 Smelling salts gas
11 000
12 Madrid coin
13 Highlands dance
18 Sicilian resort
22 College in Henrietta, NY
26 Lake Titicaca's range
27 Armenian rice dish
28 Patricia in *Hud*
29 Pierre's pate
30 Hairy wave
31 Word form of "thought"
32 XXX
34 Dirt Devil, for short
40 What anchors do
41 Bureaucratic snarl
42 Yammer
43 Go from worse to bad?
45 Kauai keepsake
47 Makes a pick
50 Pool paths
51 Big display
52 Sundial pointer
53 South African coin
54 Jejuna neighbors
55 Hebrew month
56 They get drunk in pubs
59 Sunlamp ray

BRAINSNACK® Top That

Which English muffin (1–7) doesn't have the right topping?

LETTER LINE

Put a letter in each of the squares below to make a word you won't be aware of.
The number clues refer to other words that can be made from the whole.

9 4 2 6 8 5 GRADUATES • 6 2 1 10 5 8 FINE COTTON FABRIC
5 9 6 3 METRICAL UNIT WITH UNSTRESSED-STRESSED SYLLABLES
8 5 6 3 2 1 RAIN-BEARING CLOUD • 1 5 6 7 9 8 APE-LIKE

1	2	3	4	5	6	7	8	9	10

Word Sudoku

Complete the grid so that each row, each column, and each 3 x 3 frame contains the nine letters from the black box below. The hidden nine-letter word is in the diagonal from top left to bottom right.

A B C E I L R S T

						L	E	T
		R	C	E				
	T	C		S				
B	L		T		C			E
	I				T	R	A	
	B		S					
S			I			T		
L	A	C		E	R	B		

trivia

- Who played Willy Wonka in a 1971 film?

UNCANNY TURN

Rearrange the letters of the phrase below to form a cognate anagram, one that is related or connected in meaning to the original phrase. The answer can be one or more words.

CAN ENTER

The Ex-Files

ACROSS

1 Nocturnal insect
5 Like *Biggest Loser* contestants
10 Discontinue
14 Las Vegas casino
15 Thirteen witches
16 Bishop of Rome
17 Rachel Hunter's ex
19 Model from Mogadishu
20 Novelist France
21 Big name in mustard
23 Lake Erie port
24 Danube tributary
25 Little letter
27 White knight
30 Lacunae
33 Aegean isle
35 Add employees
36 Caduceus org.
37 Dundee firth
38 ___ Croix, Quebec
39 Entre ___ (confidentially)
41 *The Hostage* playwright
43 Gripe
44 Anderson of *The X-Files*
46 Kooky
48 Sea dust, in diner slang
49 NYSE stat
53 Off the record
56 Cookbook contents
57 Hoarfrost
58 Julia Roberts' ex
60 Swan genus
61 Break out, as violence
62 About
63 Prevent from scoring
64 Fake drake
65 Uproars

DOWN

1 Friend of Danton
2 University of Maine city
3 Flowing and ebbing
4 Gets cracking
5 Spotted wildcats
6 1995 winner over Holyfield
7 Little ___ ("Loco-motion" singer)
8 Feudal slave
9 Contest forms
10 V8 juice ingredient
11 Nicole Kidman's ex
12 Aquarium fish
13 Enclosures
18 Fracas
22 Long letter
26 Off the table
27 One with subjects
28 "Symphony in Black" artist
29 Marine hazard
30 Band
31 Mine, to Pierre
32 Carrie Fisher's ex
34 ___-jongg
40 Human bondage
41 Fought
42 Originality
43 Paraguay neighbor
45 Stevedore union
47 Mme. Chanel
50 Tip over
51 Subway
52 *The Moffats* author
53 Spur
54 Tick off
55 Thornfield Hall governess
56 Taken-back item
59 Robitaille of hockey

Sudoku

Fill in the grid so that each row, each column, and each 3 x 3 frame contains every number from 1 to 9.

3				8	4			
5		2				4	8	3
					5			2
8			3	6				7
	3					6		
9				7	2			4
6			1					
7	8	4				2		6
			7	2				9

do you KNOW?

Whose children were Susanna, Hamnet and Judity?

_____

SYMBOL SUMS

Can you work out these number sums using three of these four symbols? **+ − ÷ ×**

15 ☐ 4 ☐ 4 ☐ 11 = 55

Find the Right Word

Knowing that every arrow points to a letter and that no letter can touch
another vertically, horizontally, or diagonally, find the missing letters that form
a key word in reading direction. A letter cannot be located on an arrow.
We show one letter in a circle to help you get started.

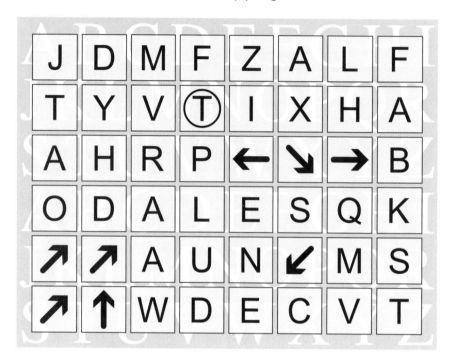

CHANGELINGS

Each of the three lines of letters below spell words for describing colors, but the letters have
been mixed up. Four letters from the first word are now in the third line, four letters from the
third word are in the second line, and four letters from the second word are in the first line.
The remaining letters are in their original places. What are the words?

A	H	U	T	U	A	R	I	S	E
C	R	A	R	W	R	E	K	E	E
P	E	Q	I	A	I	N	M	L	N

CROSSWORD **You Said It**

ACROSS

1 Get one's mitts on
5 Holmes or Couric
10 Brings in
14 Plum tomato
15 First Mrs. Trump
16 Fashion designer Saab
17 Inky black
18 Ill-mannered ones
19 Title below marquis
20 Question for the dental school student?
23 Yo-yo part
24 Kingdom east of Babylonia
25 *Big Bang Theory* types
28 Universal, for one
32 Pend
35 Like Montmartre
37 Mubarak's former domain
38 *The Mikado* wardrobe item
39 May birthstone
41 Paul Anka's "___ Beso"
42 Hang loose
44 Dreadful
45 Ruckuses
46 Monk, for one
48 Verdi's "___ Chorus"
50 Without question
52 Plain of Sharon locale
56 Famous line from *Jerry Maguire*
61 Chorus member
62 Yiddish sausage
63 Has another birthday
64 ___-do-well
65 On the up-and-up
66 Jutlander
67 Keystone ___
68 Become weatherworn
69 One Mercury orbit

DOWN

1 TV's ___ *Anatomy*
2 David in *A.I.*
3 Love affair
4 Business of checks and balances
5 About 2.2 pounds
6 State positively
7 Like a circus high wire
8 ___ *Line of Fire* (1993)
9 Flip-chart holders
10 Octoberfest souvenir
11 Half a Basque game
12 Miss
13 Put on the market
21 DC-to-NYC direction
22 Like milk cartons
26 1856 litigant Scott
27 Minute groove
29 Did some batiking
30 Facto lead-in
31 Nebraska Indians
32 ___ d'oeuvres
33 Genesis flock tender
34 Cleo barged down it
36 Tall tale
39 "Cast of thousands" member
40 Float upward
43 Swift and Fast
45 "So soon?"
47 Gather closely
49 Suffix for ghoul
51 Arab head of state
53 Baquacil target
54 *The Vampire Diaries* heroine
55 Not a medalist
56 Wrench
57 It's on a roll
58 Texas college
59 Therefore
60 Surrounded by

Futoshiki

Fill in the 5 x 5 grid with the numbers from 1 to 5 once per row and column, while following the greater-than/lesser-than symbols shown. There is only one valid solution that can be reached through logic and clear thinking alone!

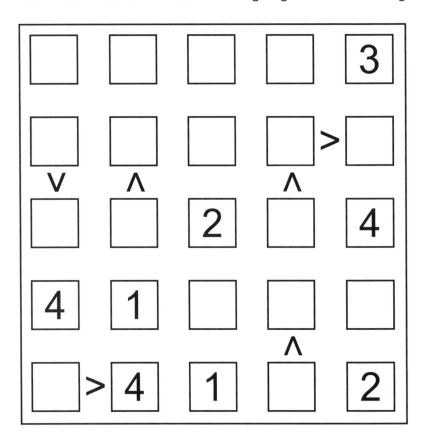

do you KNOW

What dish is arborio rice commonly used in?

_____

24

TRIVIA QUIZ Famous Firsts

At first glance, you may not think you know these answers. Take your time.
You may be surprised how much you knew in the first place!

1. In which country was the motorcar invented?
   a. Germany
   b. United States
   c. Italy
   d. France

2. Which country played host to the first modern Olympic Games in 1896?
   a. Greece
   b. Switzerland
   c. Spain
   d. Great Britain

3. What notable achievement did Sir Edmund Hillary make in 1953?
   a. The first person to reach the South Pole
   b. The first person to reach the summit of Mount Everest
   c. The first person to swim the English Channel
   d. The first person to circumnavigate the globe in a row boat

4. What food was served at the Battle Creek Sanatorium in Michigan in 1894 as the first meal of the day?
   a. Tang
   b. Biscuits and gravy
   c. Cornflakes
   d. Bacon and eggs

5. Who was the first monarch to live at Buckingham Palace?
   a. Queen Victoria
   b. William IV
   c. George II
   d. Queen Elizabeth, the Queen Mother

6. In which country did women gain the right to vote in 1893?
   a. New Zealand
   b. Austria
   c. France
   d. United States

7. Which game, according to legend, came into being when William Webb Ellis picked up the ball and ran with it in 1823?
   a. Rugby
   b. American football
   c. Table tennis
   d. Squash

8. Who packed off his first tourists to Paris in 1961, starting a holiday revolution?
   a. Anthony Eden
   b. Thomas Cook
   c. Harold Macmillan
   d. John Cheever

9. What was the nickname of Ivan, the first czar?
   a. "The Terrible"
   b. "The Beneficent"
   c. "The Garlic Eater"
   d. "The Decrepit"

Letters

Which letters are missing at the bottom of the white page?

QUICK CROSSWORD

Place the cities listed below in the crossword grid.

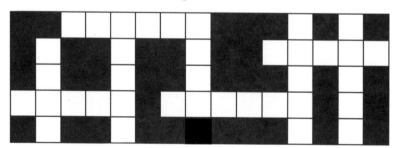

DUBLIN TOKYO DENVER CAIRO PARIS LILLE LYON NICE BOGOR

WORD SEARCH Flirt

All the words are hidden vertically, horizontally, or diagonally—in both directions. The letters that remain unused form a sentence from left to right.

```
G A I H C C N W O D T E L O R
N D N E I N G R T E N S I O N
I T T A O Y O R L D S E S E C
T A I R R M R L E I C H F O G
E L M T A I E E K R T I N L N
E G A N H W N Y V N E Q A I S
L A T E E G E N C O U N T E R
F I E R G O I O D E C R E M E
C D A U E D Y L S E F S O R J
S F I T L I S T E N T R I E E
B L I N K S J V B L U S H D C
S A N E E T O U C H D D I T T
P G I V V L K L A T E N S M I
O O S D K H E A L T H Y A T O
S M E A N E S N S M I L E C N
A H N M I G N I M R A H C D W
O M Y E R N A F F E C T I O N
A K I A D M I R A T I O N C K
```

- ADMIRATION
- ADVENTURE
- AFFECTION
- BLINK
- BLUSH
- CANDLE LIGHT
- CHARMING
- CONQUEST
- DINE
- DISCOVERY
- DRINK
- ENCOUNTER
- ENVY
- FAREWELL
- FLEETING
- GLANCE
- HEALTHY
- HEART
- INTIMATE
- JOKES
- KISS
- LETDOWN
- LISTEN
- LOVE
- NEED
- POEM
- REJECTION
- ROMANTIC
- SHY
- SMILE
- TALK
- TENSION
- TOUCH

CROSSWORD # Pen Names

ACROSS

1 Deep cut
5 Churlish
10 Leave in haste
14 Utah ski resort
15 Blakley in *Nashville*
16 Apropos of
17 Amantine Lucile Dupin's pen name
19 Mysterious radar blips
20 Police school
21 *A Man for All* ___ (1966)
23 Architect's wing
24 Back end
25 Spongy
29 Generous bestowal
32 Means of escape
33 Brazil seaport
35 Idaho motto word
36 Bed and breakfast
37 Twitch
38 Modicum
39 Lean
41 Kind of leader
43 Goddess of marriage
44 Lack of law
46 Takes off
48 California wine valley
49 Shark feature
50 Resplendent
53 Harbor deepeners
57 Amenhotep IV's god
58 Charlotte Bronte's pen name
60 Another request?
61 King Acorn of "Sonic the Hedgehog"
62 "My Way" composer
63 Where the altar is
64 Slow animal
65 Haunted house sound

DOWN

1 Lovesick
2 Baldwin in *The Departed*
3 Classical colonnade
4 Like diamond, on the Mohs scale
5 Mischievous elf
6 Promising
7 Merkel in *Daddy Longlegs*
8 Wetlands
9 FTC part
10 Braunschweiger, e.g.
11 Cecil Louis Troughton Smith's pen name
12 Like ___ of bricks
13 Fling
18 Money, slangily
22 ___ Lingus airline
25 Andrew Lloyd Webber musical
26 Bolshevik hero
27 Esther Friedman's pen name
28 Heathcliff's love
29 Streaked with color
30 Git-go
31 Movieplex drinks
34 Formalwear accessory
40 Boot camp denizen
41 A daredevil takes them
42 Internet browser button
43 Etienne Aigner product
45 Returns pro
47 Wharf
50 Wolf in *The Jungle Book*
51 At the pinnacle
52 Rock group Jethro ___
53 "Darn it!"
54 Rowlands of *Gloria*
55 Horned buglers
56 Spank
59 Sugar Loaf site

Spot the Differences

Find the nine differences in the image on the bottom right.

do you **KNOW**

Tonic water contains
which malaria
treatment?

trivia

- Which actress was born
  with the name Mironoff?

Sudoku X

Fill in the grid so that each row, each column, and each 3 x 3 frame contains every number from 1 to 9. The two main diagonals of the grid also contain every number from 1 to 9.

7		3	5			2		8
		5		4	8	1		3
		4	7	1				
				9		3	1	5
1		9		3	5	4		
	3	2	4			9	8	
2	6							4
		7	9					

do you KNOW

Where is Aung San Suu Kyi from?

CROSSWORD Alliterative Guys

ACROSS

1 Boxy sleigh
5 Scare off
10 Convertiplane, e.g.
14 King of old comics
15 Chameleon
16 Skiing aid
17 Oompa-Loompas' boss
19 Hint of the future
20 NATO members
21 Native Alaskans
23 Hazardous wind phenomenon
24 Smarmy
25 Some De La Hoya wins
28 Bening in *The Women*
31 Blueberry, for one
34 German canal city
36 Pairs
37 Genetic matter
38 Tennis opening
40 Commandment adverb
41 Bread dispensers?
43 Pluck
44 Takeout order?
45 Cooked fruit dessert
48 "March Madness" org.
50 In days of ___
51 Jordan neighbor
55 Preferably
58 Winter recreation
60 Pirate's plunder
61 Pickled peppers picker
63 Limerick language
64 Printers' daggers
65 Pond, poetically
66 *Diary of ___ Housewife* (1970)
67 Brown and Turner
68 German duck

DOWN

1 *En passant* captures
2 *David Copperfield* name
3 Nick in *Warrior*
4 Philistine giant
5 First light
6 Abel's nephew
7 Gravel weight
8 Golden Globe winner Sommer
9 The underlying cause
10 Ruined
11 *My One and Only* Tony winner
12 Sub in a tub
13 "Prime" camera accessory
18 Sergeant played by Cooper
22 Relatives
26 Agreements
27 Blockade
28 Seville chipmunk
29 Cleaver or lever
30 Tasso's patron
31 Bric-a-___
32 Golden Rule word
33 1998 National League MVP
35 Fumble, e.g.
39 Abbr. on a list
42 Like leopards
44 When Dracula sleeps
46 Mine find
47 Mad Hatter's table item
49 Memo "pronto"
52 Age, as cheese
53 Immobile
54 Emulate a toady
55 Intestinal sections
56 Van Brocklin of football
57 Mazar in *GoodFellas*
58 *Once and Again* actress Ward
59 Humphries of the NBA
62 Bart Simpson's age

BRAINSNACK® **Medication**

Which combination of pills will the patient have to take next time?

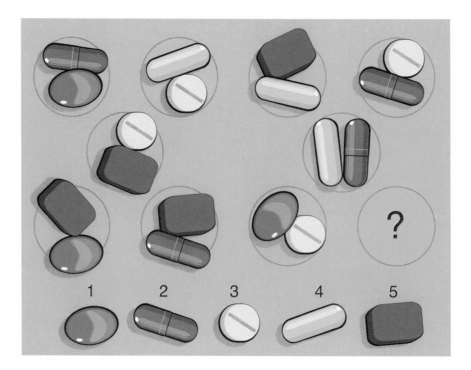

QUICK WORD SEARCH

Find the flowers and trees listed below in the word search grid.

```
M U I L L A N E M O N E O A K
Z D I H C R O C U S O L I V E
H O S T A I L H A D Y N O E P
X O L H P F H S O M S O C Z P
C A L I L W O R R A Y L L O H
```

ALLIUM ANEMONE COSMOS CROCUS DAHLIA HOLLY HOSTA
LILAC PEONY PHLOX OAK OLIVE ORCHID YARROW

Kakuro

Each number in a black area is the sum of the numbers that you have to enter in the next empty boxes. The empty boxes that make up the sum are called a run. The sum of the across run is written above the diagonal in the black area, and the sum of the down run is written below the diagonal. Runs can only contain the numbers 1 through 9, and each number in a run can only be used once. The gray boxes only contain odd numbers and the white only even numbers.

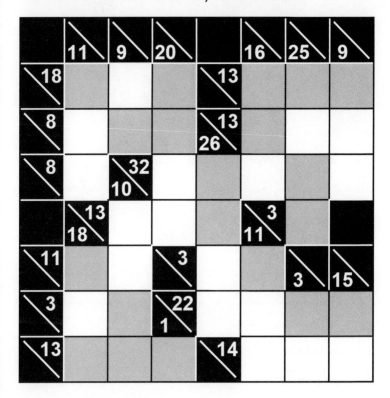

SANDWICH

What four-letter word belongs between the word at left and the word at right, so that the first and second word, and the second and third word, each form a common compound word or phrase?

B O B _ _ _ _ S P I N

CROSSWORD ▶ Title Role Players

ACROSS

1 Type of brakes or jockeys
5 Impart learning
10 Capt. Hook's aide
14 Tennis legend Arthur
15 Prefix for electric
16 Do in
17 *Michael Collins* star
19 *Casablanca* heroine
20 Wins by charm
21 Dewhurst in *The Cowboys*
23 PAC that's packing
24 Poly partner
25 Cut short
29 De Mornay in *The Winner*
32 Platte River natives
33 Just beat (out)
35 Neophyte
36 Russian jet
37 Subside
38 1920 play about robots
39 *Law & Order: SVU* star
41 "Eight Days ___": Beatles
43 Necessity
44 Tia in *Wayne's World*
46 Flockhart of *Ally McBeal*
48 ___ & Chandon
49 "One Mic" rapper
50 Albumin, for one
53 Williams and Rolle
57 Treasure chest filler
58 *Frida* star
60 To be, in Blois
61 Dancer Ailey
62 ___-dieu (kneeler)
63 Green car in *Cars 2*
64 Spikes
65 Dispatch

DOWN

1 Glen
2 "Love ___ the Air" (1978 hit)
3 Planking fish
4 Establishes firmly
5 "Kiss Me in ___": Streisand
6 Argus has 100
7 Classified material?
8 Hook's pursuer
9 Roasted, in a way
10 Hash house pan
11 *Hannah Montana* star
12 What ___ can I say?
13 Enthusiasm
18 Former Japanese capital
22 It may result in a smash hit
25 Elvis Costello's "God's ___"
26 Branch office on *The Office*
27 *Sherlock Holmes in New York* star
28 *My Fair Lady* composer
29 Renaissance fiddle
30 Pie part
31 Major artery
34 Opposite NbW
40 Standardbred horse
41 Craftsman
42 Jayhawkers
43 Accidents
45 Wide shoe width
47 Narrow wood strip
50 Accused's answer
51 College drill team
52 *The Lion King* lioness
53 Pianist Gilels
54 Jane who loved Rochester
55 Bit attachment
56 Agenda, informally
59 Caesar's 56

Hourglass

Starting in the middle, each word in the top half has the letters of the word below it, plus a new letter, and each word in the bottom half has the letters of the word above it, plus a new letter.

(1) Small army unit

(2) Tease

(3) Made from dough

(4) Lyric poet

(5) Short for Abraham

(6) Deep yellow color

(7) Sculpture rock

(8) Pedestrian

Sudoku Twin

Fill in the grid so that each row, each column, and each 3 x 3 frame contains every number from 1 to 9. A sudoku twin is two connected 9 x 9 sudokus.

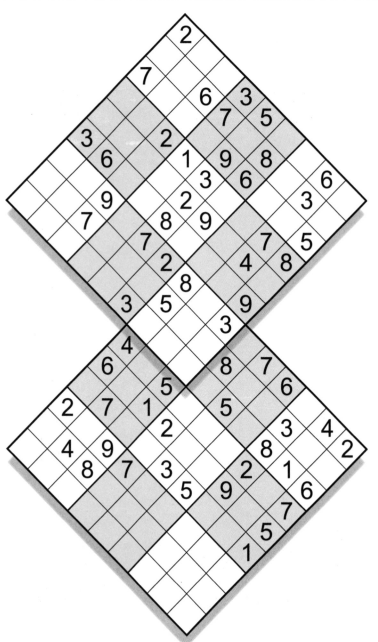

CROSSWORD Themeless 2

ACROSS

1 Rafa's house
5 Do a triple axel, say
10 Botanist Gray and namesakes
14 Its capital was Susa
15 Offered a hand to
16 Jumping a line, e.g.
17 Magic Kingdom locale
19 *L.A. Story* actress
20 Level of command
21 *Lady and the Tramp* cats
23 Case-harden
24 Margery Daw's board
25 Crown from Cartier
27 Agitated state
30 Great multitude
33 Root words?
35 "John ___ Tractor": Judds
36 19th Greek letter
37 Elan
39 Expurgate
40 Palmer in *Moll Flanders*
42 *Deus* ___ (1976 sci-fi novel)
43 Nancy Drew's friend
44 Have in view
46 Garden bower
48 Resident doctor
50 Was revolting?
54 Popular pudding
56 Silo resident
57 Cuba or Crete, e.g.
58 Anne Tyler's *The ___ Tourist*
60 Security of a kind
61 Colonial diplomat Silas
62 Berlin senior
63 Hindmost
64 Bass-baritone Simon
65 Prerequisite

DOWN

1 Surrenders formally
2 2010 Mia Wasikowska role
3 Malia Obama's sister
4 General pardon
5 Japanese farewell
6 Potter's need
7 Monroe in *Cold Mountain*
8 Inflexible
9 Made a watery swirl
10 Vivify
11 *West Side Story* song
12 Duck genus
13 Loudness unit
18 Aristocratic Wells race
22 Out of the way
24 Like North Africa
26 Hindu royalty
28 Greek strife goddess
29 Biopic about John Reed
30 Legendary Hun king
31 Picnic hamperer
32 10 and 15, to 5
34 Battle souvenir
37 Bean or horse
38 Archipelago off Scotland
41 Sparing the rod
43 Pierce in *GoldenEye*
45 The teens, for one
47 River into the Seine
49 Meet events
51 Championship
52 Put in high spirits
53 Took a line out
54 Cash drawer
55 China setting
56 Excavation
59 Growltiger, for one

Sport Maze

Draw the shortest way from the ball to the goal. You can only move along vertical and horizontal lines, not along diagonal lines. The figure on each square indicates the number of squares the ball must move in the same direction. You can change direction at each stop.

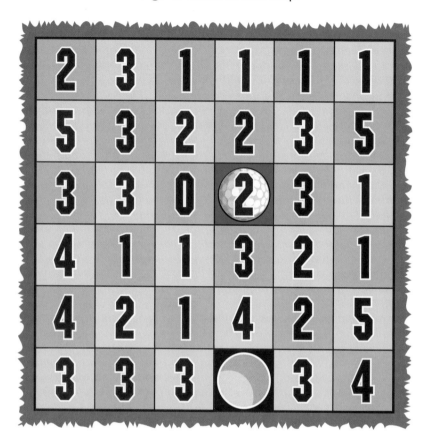

ONE LETTER LESS OR MORE

The word on the right side contains the letters of the word on the left side, plus or minus the letter in the middle. One letter is already in the right place.

E L E C T I N G -I ☐ ☐ G ☐ ☐ ☐ ☐

WORD SEARCH **Jack Nicholson**

All the words are hidden vertically, horizontally, or diagonally—in both directions. The letters that remain unused form a sentence from left to right.

```
E T C D O O W Y L L O H J S A
M H R N C K H N N L I C N R H
I E Y E O S T N L A S O O E O
T S B W A U U U N B O I S D I
C H A Y F C O B A T M A N I R
A I B O F C Y L R E A A L R A
E N Y R O E D A T K R Y R Y N
H I K K H S C E B S I O E S E
S N I R G S T R R A N B A A C
C G L E O T O E R B E W O E S
F Y L H K I K M C O L O N E L
S M E G E A A M E R I C A N N
G M R W L E J I R A T I O N T
W O O O G E T R H E R W I T H
I T F M N R U B T R A E H R O
T B D E E W N O R I E R T D E
C N I N R R O A N D A L P A C
H I N G O L D E N G L O B E O
```

- AMERICAN
- BASKETBALL
- BATMAN
- BRIMMER
- BUNNY
- CARTOONS
- COLONEL
- COWBOY
- CRY BABY KILLER
- EASY RIDER
- GOFER
- GOLDEN GLOBE
- GRIN
- HEARTBURN
- HOFFA
- HOLLYWOOD
- IRONWEED
- JAKE
- LAKERS
- MARINE
- MARS
- NEW YORK
- OSCAR
- SCENARIO
- SUCCESS
- THE SHINING
- TIME
- TOMMY
- WITCH
- WOMEN
- YOUTH

Alliterative Gals

ACROSS

1 Tiff
5 Cracks a book
10 *The Good Earth* wife
14 Essence
15 Projecting window
16 Raise to the third power
17 *La Dolce Vita* star
19 Prefix meaning height
20 Daredevil's desire
21 *Sleepless in Seattle* star
23 Musical set in Baghdad
26 Bridal accessory
27 Draws a breath
29 *I Was a ___ Werewolf* (1957)
32 Sonogram, e.g.
33 Ostrichlike birds
35 Illegal way to go
36 Attenborough's title
37 Etcher's need
38 Whippersnapper
39 Bond's school
41 Didn't take part (with "out")
43 Soccer's "Black Pearl"
44 They just say no
46 Archrival
48 Ward in *The Fugitive*
49 Medieval bodice
50 Writer's starting point
53 Place for a coin
54 Amateurs' opposites
55 1931 star of *Mata Hari*
60 Pitchfork part
61 Glowing piece of coal
62 One getting bags of fan mail
63 Eerie sign
64 Buffalo player
65 Scruff of the neck

DOWN

1 Fat farm
2 Code entered on a keypad
3 From ___ Z
4 Uma in *Batman & Robin*
5 Poultry purchase
6 Scandinavian explorer
7 Objective
8 Make judgments
9 They bear arms
10 Small wind instrument
11 *Xena: Warrior Princess* star
12 Magical opener
13 Inert gas in vacuum tubes
18 Richard of *Moonraker*
22 "Well I'll be!"
23 Played post office
24 Foment
25 *Total Recall* star
28 Harbor sights
29 Accepted
30 Soccer position
31 First in line to the throne
34 Tolkien's Treebeard
40 Leslie in *Airplane!*
41 Florida fruits
42 State
43 Have relevance
45 *There Will Be Blood* preacher
47 Synthesizer inventor
50 Vision: Comb. form
51 ___ and Thummim
52 Humorist Bombeck
53 Gang follower
56 Tide's retreat
57 No. on a food label
58 Conk on the noggin
59 Jai-alai cheer

BRAINSNACK® Number Cube

Which number should replace the question mark?

19 11 11 ? 12

DOODLE PUZZLE

A doodle puzzle is a combination of images, letters, and/or numbers that represent a word or a concept. If you cannot solve a doodle puzzle, do not look at the answer right away. Think hard—and outside the box.

Triangle Teaser

Which number is missing from triangle B?

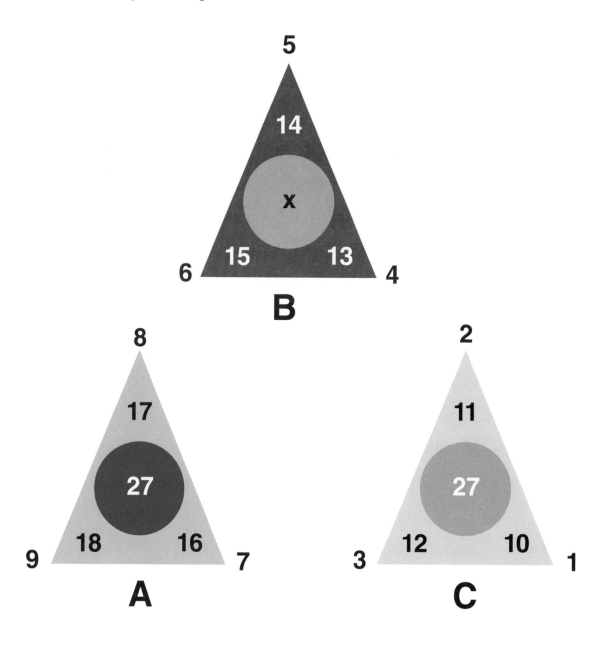

Word Sudoku

Complete the grid so that each row, each column, and each 3 x 3 frame contains the nine letters from the black box below. The hidden nine-letter word is in the diagonal from top left to bottom right.

E	G	H	I	J	L	M	P	T

	J	H	M		E		G	I
P	I			H	J		L	E
T				I	G			J
J		P				L		
M						E		G
			G				T	
E			I	J				P
		T					H	

do you KNOW?

Who painted "The Birth of Venus" in 1486?

_____

UNCANNY TURN

Rearrange the letters of the phrase below to form a cognate anagram, one that is related or connected in meaning to the original phrase. The answer can be one or more words.

A FLARING END

Things To Be Thankful For

ACROSS

1 Annika Sorenstam is a pro at this
5 "Shucks!"
9 What a happy dog does
12 Butter substitute
13 It follows ready and willing
14 Gorilla
15 Ingredient in some batters
16 Great getaway
18 Open to women and men
20 ___ space
21 The dishwasher is a ___ convenience
24 An egg, for one
25 Come up
26 Furry friends
27 Tech company
28 Center
29 Cooking spray brand
32 No place like ____
34 Coming ___ (2 words)
36 Tease
39 Well-being
40 Plant ___ (2 words)
41 Form of bacteria
42 Light that gives life
44 Spring bloom
48 White-tailed eagle
49 Mrs. Clooney
50 Name linked with lemon, commercially
51 The Partridge Family actress Susan
52 Makes lace
53 Cry out

DOWN

1 Gooey pile
2 Old
3 *Go Set a Watchman* author Harper
4 The Armed ___
5 Black bird
6 Leave ___ taste in the mouth (2 words)
7 *Cake Boss* network
8 Tall grass found by the beach (2 words)
9 Ralph ___, John Sr. on The Waltons
10 "I'm ___ and I didn't know it!" (2 words)
11 Romance or mystery, for example
17 Tablet after a big meal
19 ___-Ida potatoes
21 ___ Tai
22 Earth is one
23 Poorly lit
24 Diploma alternative
26 Pastry dessert
28 French Mrs. (abbr.)
29 Buddy
30 Famous TV contest (abbr.)
31 Apathetic expression
32 Tools for the garden
33 Familiar (2 words)
34 Contraction before "the ramparts"
35 Relatives
36 "___ the joint"
37 ___ thing (2 words)
38 Her phone number is 867-5309
39 Stilettos
41 Pesky bug
43 "___ little teapot" (2 words)
45 Regret
46 Not feeling great
47 Slang for "How's it going?"

Binairo

Complete the grid with zeros and ones until there are 6 zeros and 6 ones in every row and every column. No more than two of the same number can be next to or under each other. Rows or columns with exactly the same content are not allowed. There is only one valid solution.

		I			I						
	I	I		O							O
			I			I		O			
	I						O	O			
						O		O			
I		O		O			O	O			
		I									
	I		O		I			I	I		
					O						
	O		O				I	I			
I	O			O	O				O		

trivia

- Who played Dracula in the 1931 movie?

LETTERBLOCKS

Move the letterblocks around so that words associated with winter are formed on the top and bottom rows. In some blocks the letter from the top row has been switched with the letter from the bottom row.

Splish Splash

Don't just stand there dipping your toe into the side of the pool.
Let's start off by jumping into the deep end with this mixed round of questions.

1. Name the actor, famous for playing Tarzan, who was the first man to swim 100 meters in under a minute.

2. What is the second-fastest swimming stroke?

3. Which swimming stroke begins the first leg of a 4 x 100-meter medley relay?

4. What is the longest distance among swimming events held at the Olympic Games?

5. Captain Matthew Webb, the first man to swim the English Channel without a life jacket, later died trying to swim the rapids of which waterfall?

6. In 1979, Diana Nyad became the first person to swim to Florida from which Caribbean island?

7. What massive land mammal can swim 20 miles a day?

8. What great American inventor is credited with inventing swim fins?

9. What bodily fluid does the average human produce enough of in a lifetime to fill two swimming pools?

10. The earliest-known goggle artifacts, estimated to have been made in the 1300s, were crafted from what type of polished shell?

11. Swimming dates back to 2500 BCE and can be seen in ancient Egyptian drawings. What stroke goes back to the Stone Ages, but wasn't competitively swam at the Olympics until 1904?

12. How long can free divers hold their breath?

CROSSWORD # Explorers

ACROSS

1 Cross
5 Brit baby buggy
9 Shutterbug's lens
14 *Vissi d'____*: Puccini
15 Labor on the docks
16 Find loathsome
17 Explorer of Newfoundland
19 Mirthful
20 ____ fish (clown fish)
21 Puzzling posers
23 *Ars Poetica* author
24 "I need it yesterday!" initials
25 Deteriorates
27 Double-wide
30 Leisurely catch rays
33 Unmoved one
35 *Fiesque* composer
36 ____ pro nobis
37 Egypt/Syria: 1958–61
38 *As ____* (Alicia Keys album)
39 Ego
41 Mall indulgence
43 Sicilian resort
44 Flockhart of *Ally McBeal*
46 Morse dashes
48 Himalayan mystery
49 Eat crow
53 A square has four
56 *Princess ____* (1994)
57 Sheepish
58 13th-century explorer of Asia
60 Passover meal
61 Provo locale
62 Welsh form of John
63 Head lock
64 Up for it
65 Bear lairs

DOWN

1 Punjab prince
2 Maine college town
3 Survey blank
4 *Hamlet* setting
5 Holst subjects
6 *Sticks and Bones* dramatist
7 Commotion
8 Dole (with "out")
9 Tomei in *Anger Management*
10 Mrs. John Adams
11 Quebec City founder
12 *Bottled in Blonde* author Jaffe
13 Scraps
18 Chanel or Crisp
22 Drugbuster
26 Dome-shaped Buddhist memorial
27 Dead on one's feet
28 Vigorous spirit
29 Eternal City
30 Skinny-necked pear
31 Square measure
32 First U.S. woman in space
34 Row the boat
40 Ralph in *The English Patient*
41 To-do
42 Otitis
43 Flew the coop
45 Stampede beasts
47 Man of the hour
50 Better than
51 "Ryan Express" of baseball
52 Roger Rabbit and others
53 Consumer's concern
54 CB word
55 Full of oneself
56 Study at the last minute
59 Strain ____ gnat

Horoscope

Fill in the grid so that every row, every column and every frame of six boxes contains six different symbols: health, work, money, happiness, family, and love. Look at the row or column that corresponds with your sign of the zodiac and find out which of the six symbols are important for you today. The symbols appear in increasing order of importance (1–6). It's up to you to translate the meaning of each symbol to your specific situation.

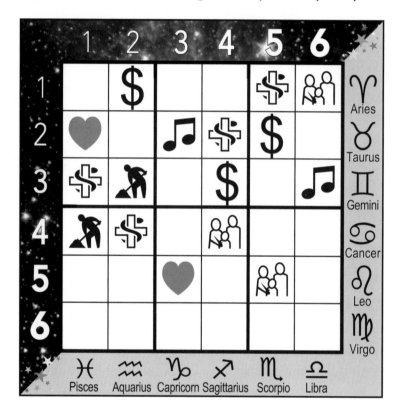

delete ONE

Delete one letter from
NAME ALIGNED
and rearrange the rest to find someone popular.

_____

LETTERBLOCKS

Move the letterblocks around so that words associated with thrillers are formed on the top and bottom rows. In some blocks the letter from the top row has been switched with the letter from the bottom row.

Sudoku

Fill in the grid so that each row, each column, and each 3 x 3 frame
contains every number from 1 to 9.

				3				
9					8			
	4					7		
		1						
6		3	7	1	4			
	8		9		6		7	
	6	5		8	1		9	2
8	2	9	3	6	5			
	3			7		6		8

trivia

- What did St. Patrick reputedly banish from Ireland?

_____

SYMBOL SUMS

Can you work out these number sums using three of these four symbols? **+ − ÷ ×**

2 ☐ 1 ☐ 6 ☐ 6 = 48

End to End

ACROSS

1 Justice Bader Ginsburg
5 Daytime dramas
10 Sign for a fortune-teller
14 1970s do
15 Gold measure
16 Unmixed
17 Jeep Wrangler, for one
19 Retin-A target
20 Black Friday sights
21 Had a sandwich, perhaps
23 Alma mater
26 Part of DIY
27 Start a Model A
29 Make good as new
32 Work up
33 Artist's aid
35 "Wear ___ Love Like Heaven": Donovan
36 Currency-stabilizing org.
37 Vote in a legislative body
38 Wharton degree
39 Nut part
41 Lively dances
43 Cores
44 Pizazz
46 Mr. Peanut's eyeglass
48 Sideless wagon
49 Down below
50 Warms leftovers
53 They're big on Bugs
54 Greek vowels
55 Confrontation
60 Lose feathers
61 The press
62 SeaWorld whale
63 Lowdown
64 Dalmatian features
65 Low card

DOWN

1 Vallone in *The Godfather: Part III*
2 Interstellar craft
3 "Da Crime Family" rap trio
4 Insulin, for example
5 Azure
6 Louts
7 Orinoco tributary
8 Lumberjack Bunyan
9 German pastry
10 Murkiness
11 Way more than necessary
12 Fish-eating fowl
13 Must have
18 Match packet
22 Denials
23 Pinch pennies
24 Battle of Balaclava setting
25 Cremora alternative
28 Name on a check
29 Sphere
30 Implosion result
31 Pencil end
34 Get the point
40 Has the nerve
41 Tempos
42 Beethoven works
43 Whiz with an ego
45 Hollywood talent agcy.
47 Franco in *Camelot*
50 "Do ___ fa ..."
51 William Pitt's alma mater
52 Trickle down
53 Correct copy
56 Hoo-ha
57 Botch
58 All-Star pitcher
59 Journal unit

BRAINSNACK® **Read the Flags**

Which signal flag (1–5) should replace the question mark in order to complete this unique series?

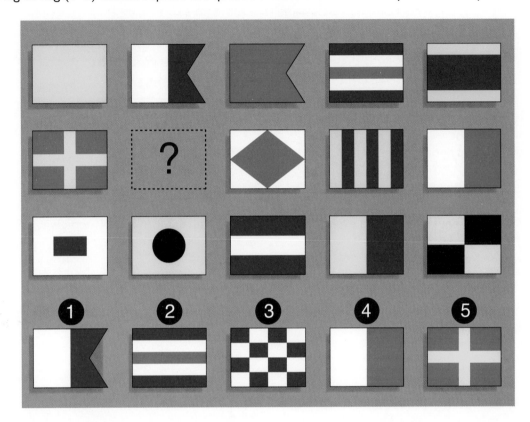

CHANGELINGS

Each of the three lines of letters below spell words that have charitable connection, but the letters have been mixed up. Four letters from the first word are now in the third line, four letters from the third word are in the second line, and four letters from the second word are in the first line. The remaining letters are in their original places. What are the words?

C S N P P I B U V E

B U F C O R T I L E

O E N E T I R I A T

The Doctor Is In

By 1957, Theodor Geisel, better known as Dr. Seuss, had been writing children's stories for 20 years, with 12 books to his name. But that year saw the release of two of his classics, *The Cat in the Hat* and *How the Grinch Stole Christmas!*

WHAT DO YOU REMEMBER OF THE FANTASTICAL CHAOS OF THE SEUSSIAN UNIVERSE?

1 What red-suited mischief-makers does the Cat in the Hat introduce to Sally and her brother?

2 Who keeps saying no to everything the Cat suggests?

3 How many sizes too small is the Grinch's heart?

4 This little Who discovers the Grinch stealing her family's Christmas tree.

5 Who offers the narrator food in *Green Eggs and Ham*?

6 This was the first Dr. Seuss book, published in 1937.

7 This 1961 title opens with a tale about silly creatures with stars on their bellies.

8 What reptile in a 1958 book was master of all he surveyed?

9 What is the name of the elephant who hears a Who?

10 This 1960 book featured swimmers in the title.

11 Where does the Grinch live?

12 What did Thing 1 and Thing 2 fly in the house?

Number Cluster

Cubes showing numbers have been placed on the grid below, with some spaces left empty. Can you complete the grid by creating runs of the same number and of the same length as the number? So, where a cube with number 5 has been included on the grid, you need to create a run of five number 5's, including the cube already shown. The run can be horizontal, vertical, or both horizontal and vertical.

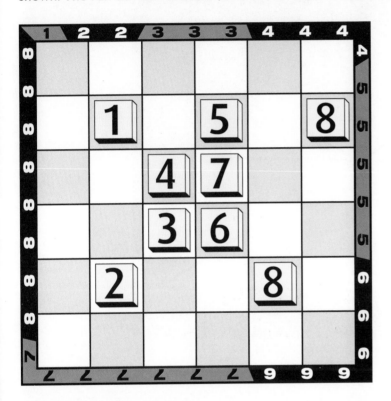

delete ONE

Delete one letter from
OPTICALLY HONE,
rearrange the rest, and sound it out!

_____

DOODLE PUZZLE

A doodle puzzle is a combination of images, letters, and/or numbers that represent a word or a concept. If you cannot solve a doodle puzzle, do not look at the answer right away. Think hard—and outside the box.

Tricky Triangles

How many triangles can you see?

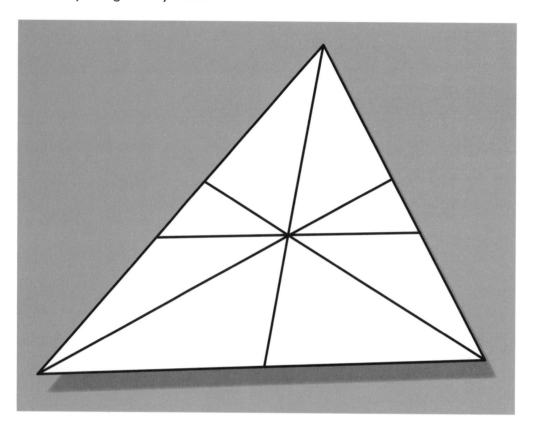

WORD WALL

Beginning at the left side of the wall, make a word by adding one group of letters from each column as you move left to right. When you have found the first word, go back to the second column and start the next word, gathering one group of letters from each column and so on until all the letters are used to make six words.

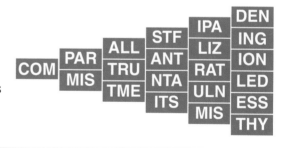

CROSSWORD Golden Globe Winners

ACROSS

1 *As I Lay Dying* father
5 Wife's sibling
10 Equipment
14 Pillow stuffing
15 Kelly in *Chaplin*
16 Celestial bear
17 "Break ___!"
18 Protozoan, e.g.
19 Not for
20 *The X-Files* Golden Globe winner
23 Join the Army
24 Legal scholar's deg.
25 Phaser setting
27 Came clean
31 Tie down
34 Tug-of-war must
36 *Absolutely Fabulous* role
37 Poetic dusk
38 Post products
40 In honor of
41 Sister of Melpomene
43 Typical Hopi village site
44 Expense
45 Curve cutters
47 Eternally
49 Hagen of the stage
50 *Seinfeld* character
54 *Friends* Golden Globe winner
60 Ocular layer
61 Palm branch
62 Ice-cream type
63 Pass judgment on
64 Espresso variation
65 "So what ___ is new?"
66 Crucifix inscription
67 Knockout drops
68 Turned blue, perhaps

DOWN

1 Maxim
2 *Baywatch* actress Gena Lee
3 Nifty
4 Official language of Fiji
5 Childish
6 Time for a bite
7 Filmmaker Wertmuller
8 Islands of Eire
9 Walk like a duck
10 Circumspect
11 Sea eagles
12 Concerning
13 "A Day Without ___": Enya

21 Ending for clarinet
22 Munchkins
26 Comparison figures
27 Car contract
28 Inventory method, for short
29 Seth begat him
30 Compact Dodge
31 Cobb in *On the Waterfront*
32 Gaseous prefix
33 Get caught
35 ___ Wee Reese
38 Raccoon's kin
39 Perfume fragrance
42 Dangerous wave

44 Went to sleep, slangily
46 Shilly-shally
48 Ransom ___ Olds
51 Campania locale
52 Ancient Scandinavian
53 Finished
54 Dench of *84 Charing Cross Road*
55 Smooth
56 ___-do-well
57 Part of QED
58 *Zuckerman Bound* author
59 Texas hold'em stake

Name the Sport

ACROSS

1 Bear hands
5 Matter of faith
10 Belter's tools
14 Fit to ___
15 Steamboat site
16 *Happy Days* actor
17 Sport of digs and spikes
19 Try
20 Nonstop
21 They're sent to editors
23 Tucson's environs
24 Sixth Hebrew month
25 Peregrinate
27 Tasteless
30 Cornfield cries
33 Heaps kudos on
35 Joint point
36 "Love ___ Madly": the Doors
37 Actress Dawn Chong
38 ___ Alamos
39 Quarter
41 Lavender
43 11th President
44 Contempt
46 Tie down
48 "I Whistle a Happy ___"
49 Stall talk
53 Duke of Cambridge
56 Seafood item
57 Director Kazan
58 Sport with a shot clock
60 "___ No Money": Cash
61 Modem messages
62 Creative starting point
63 Fury
64 Bumper dings
65 Arbor abode

1	2	3	4		5	6	7	8	9		10	11	12	13
14					15						16			
17				18							19			
20								21		22				
23							24							
			25		26	27						28	29	
30	31	32			33		34				35			
36					37						38			
39			40		41				42		43			
44				45				46		47				
		48							49			50	51	52
53	54				55		56							
57					58		59							
60					61						62			
63					64						65			

DOWN

1 Blacktopped
2 Do penance
3 Does some pipe repairs
4 Strangelove's portrayer
5 Formal glassware
6 BBQ favorites
7 Little Stowe girl
8 Farmer's place, in song
9 Siege site of 1428
10 Refrain from
11 Sport where a bunny is a goal
12 Story teller
13 Audible cries
18 Architect Saarinen
22 Super Sunday scores
26 Sausalito's county
27 Meriting a ten
28 Pedestal figure
29 Secretary's workplace
30 Lake in Cameroon
31 Word form for "air"
32 Sport with riding time
34 "Friendly Skies" airline: Abbr.
40 Flatter excessively
41 Late riser
42 Neutralizes
43 Ripa's former cohost
45 Young Skywalker's nickname
47 Sliding feature of a scull
50 Clearing
51 Pebble Beach targets
52 Melon-crushing sound
53 Everyday use
54 Mozart opera princess
55 Jerry Herman musical
56 Variety-show segment
59 ___ Francisco

BRAINSNACK® Keeping Score

Which digit should replace the question mark in the score?

CLOCKWISE

The answers to the clues from 1 to 12 are all seven-letter words that end with the letter D. When you have solved the puzzle correctly, working clockwise from 1, the 12 letters in the outer circle will spell a word that can be applied to formulaic matters.

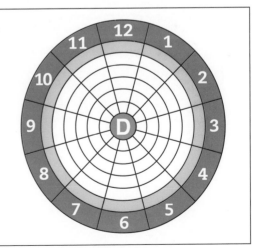

1 Duck
2 A defendant
3 Gland
4 From an egg
5 At large
6 Damaged
7 Agitated
8 Browned by heat
9 Breathed in
10 Pattern
11 Insured
12 Fastened

Frankenstein

All the words are hidden vertically, horizontally, or diagonally—in both directions. The letters that remain unused form a sentence from left to right.

```
H I D E O U S L F R A N K E N
S T D E T D O G S L E D I N E
I S T N E N O R Y B D R O L L
H G B S E S P R O C E N A Y C
M E R S H I E O F T H N E R R
D R O E S D R A M A I O H O I
R M T N E Y E F C U T O O T C
E A H I C D D R R T H A R A C
F N E L I A E U T C R V R R I
U Y R C E A T D T E D E I O T
G T I E H E M E I S D N B B C
E U O D N S R T E R R E L A R
S N O E N I T S U J B G E L A
T T H E F C O M P A N I O N K
M O N M S S S E L E F I L C T
D N A L R E Z T I W S E I R I
T S W I L L I A M N O S I R P
E L F F G O T H I C W O M A N
```

- ARCTIC CIRCLE
- BRIDE
- BROTHER
- COMPANION
- CORPSES
- DECLINE
- DOG SLED
- DRAMA
- FILM
- FIRE
- FRIEND
- GENEVA
- GERMANY
- GOTHIC
- HATE
- HIDEOUS
- HORRIBLE
- ICE SHEET
- JUSTINE
- LABORATORY
- LIFELESS
- LONESOME
- LORD BYRON
- MURDER
- PRISON
- REFUGE
- RUIN
- SICK
- STUDY
- SUICIDE
- SWITZERLAND
- WILLIAM
- WOMAN

Futoshiki

Fill in the 5 x 5 grid with the numbers from 1 to 5 once per row and column, while following the greater-than/lesser-than symbols shown. There is only one valid solution that can be reached through logic and clear thinking alone!

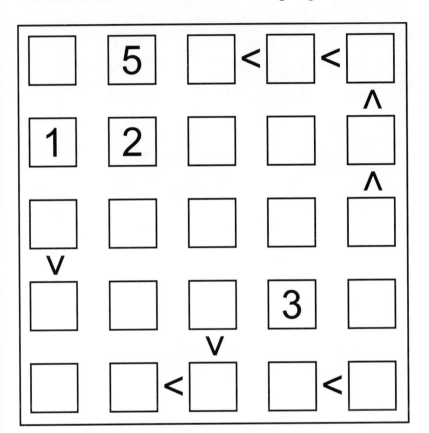

do you KNOW?

Which fabric was first made in Nîmes?

_____

TRIANAGRAM

Three-word groups of anagrams are also called triplets or trianagrams.
Complete the group:

E I G H T H S _ _ _ _ _ _ _   _ _ _ _ _ _ _

Part of ...

ACROSS

1 Under covers
5 "Champion" of Spain
10 Rent-___ (security guard)
14 Chocolate sauce
15 Seine tributary
16 Lady wooed by a swan
17 Part of ASCAP
19 Chess great Nimzovich
20 Certain vegetable cooker
21 Big chip off the old block?
23 New York socialite Kempner
24 Final
25 Non-appearance
29 Tentacled fish
32 Frilly
33 The best
35 Before long, to Shakespeare
36 "Big Daddy" Amin
37 Cauldron
38 Addams Family cousin
39 Man has seven
41 Was broadcast
43 Look badly?
44 Next year's alumnae
46 L'enfant prodigue composer
48 Mariners, slangily
49 Battle of ___ Juan Hill
50 Ascended
53 Lourdes hope
57 Existence
58 Part of SONAR
60 Sale caveat
61 Pretty up
62 Emilia's murderer
63 Tempo
64 Bowling site
65 Simmer down

DOWN

1 Sound boosters
2 Wrestling match
3 Hamburg river
4 Kim of Philly
5 Inherent quality
6 Cowardly Lion actor
7 George in Kramer vs. Kramer
8 Cross letters
9 Flight portion
10 Mobile state
11 Part of MC
12 Unpleasant aura
13 Sign of hunger
18 Bowie's model wife
22 Program file extension
25 Stage name
26 ___ of honor
27 Part of UNESCO
28 "Teddy Bear" singer
29 Was Lear
30 Study aids
31 Race listing
34 Cup handle
40 Blue-eyed cat
41 Arms stash
42 Decorative patterns
43 Asylum resident
45 Ghostly form
47 Silent film star Theda
50 Thunder sound
51 Edelstein of House
52 Man Ray's genre
53 Muddy mess
54 Trendy parting
55 RCA's victrola, for one
56 Organic compound
59 Max ___ Sydow

Keep Going

Start on a blank square of your choice and connect as many blank squares as possible with one single continuous line. You can only connect squares along vertical and horizontal lines, not along diagonal lines. You must continue the connecting lineup until the next obstacle, i.e., the border of the box, a black square, or a square that already has been used. You can change direction at any obstacle you meet. Each square can only be used once. The number of blank squares that will be left unused is marked in the upper square. There is more than one solution. We only show one solution.

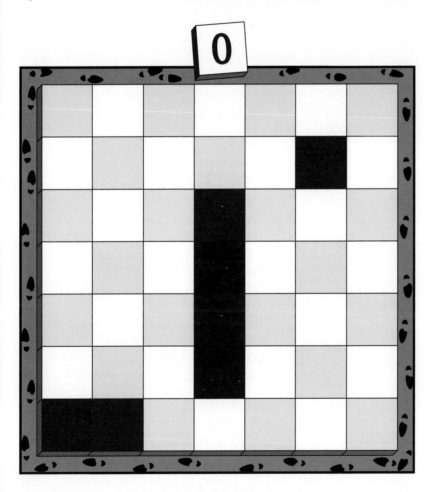

Hear, Here!

Words that sound alike are called homophones, and some—
like *oral* (of speech) and *aural* (of hearing)—are trickier to differentiate than others.
Take this ear-bending quiz, and then check your answers.

. . . .

1. **gambol** ('gam-buhl) *v.*—A: frolic.
   B: take a risk. C: walk with a limp.

2. **humerus** ('hyoo-mer-us) *n.*—
   A: arm bone. B: comic.
   C: rich garden soil.

3. **discrete** (dis-'kreet) *adj.*—
   A: prudent. B: circular.
   C: separate.

4. **carrel** ('kayh-rel) *n.*—
   A: study alcove. B: Yuletide song.
   C: cattle pen.

5. **appellation** (ah-pel-'lay-shun)
   n.—A: mountain chain.
   B: name or title.
   C: sincere entreaty.

6. **pore** ('pohr) *v.*—
   A: read attentively.
   B: open slowly.
   C: rain down in buckets.

7. **dissent** (dih-'sent) *n.*—
   A: downward slope.
   B: cancellation.
   C: difference of opinion.

8. **straiten** ('strayt-in) *v.*—
   A: tidy up. B: hem in.
   C: become horizontal.

9. **martial** ('mahr-shul) *adj.*—
   A: of marriage.
   B: relating to war.
   C: upholding law.

10. **gild** ('gild) *v.*—
    A: form a trade union.
    B: cover with a thin layer of gold.
    C: feel remorse.

11. **complementary** (kom-pleh-
    'men-tuh-ree) *adj.*—
    A: given free as a courtesy.
    B: flattering with praise.
    C: having mutually completing
    parts.

12. **signet** ('sig-nit) *n.*—A: swan.
    B: seal. C: skunk.

13. **principle** ('prin-si-puhl) *n.*—
    A: school chief.
    B: rule or doctrine.
    C: sum earning interest.

14. **pallet** ('pal-lit) *n.*—
    A: sense of taste. B: bed.
    C: painter's board.

15. **augur** ('aw-ger) *n.*—
    A: drill bit. B: heat wave.
    C: reader of omens.

Sport Maze

Draw the shortest way from the ball to the goal. You can only move along vertical and horizontal lines, not along diagonal lines. The figure on each square indicates the number of squares the ball must move in the same direction. You can change direction at each stop.

3	2	2	3	⚫	5
2	3	2	2	4	5
5	3	0	1	3	5
5	3	1	3	2	2
1	1	3	4	2	2
2	3	5	2	3	1

do you KNOW?

Which sport was first called Mintonette?

_____

ONE LETTER LESS OR MORE

The word on the right side contains the letters of the word on the left side, plus or minus the letter in the middle. One letter is already in the right place.

T H I R T E E N -T- ☐ E ☐ ☐ ☐ ☐

A Number of Films

ACROSS

1 Affleck and Stein
5 Hoofs it
10 Coarse file
14 "I cannot tell ___"
15 Maxwell Smart, e.g.
16 Indy winner Luyendyk
17 Judicial bench
18 1999 George Clooney film
20 Ferrera of *Ugly Betty*
22 Not hard to understand
23 New Age pianist John
24 Tampa-to-Orlando dir.
25 Wardrobe
28 Rivet
32 NFL officials
33 Fixes holes in hose
35 Agitated condition
36 Center front?
37 Cardinal
38 Guido's note
39 "___ Only Just Begun": Carpenters
41 Ruination
43 Ways away
44 Inga in *North and South*
46 Down-to-earth type
48 Holy city of Iran
49 *The Secret of ___ Inish* (1995)
50 Reinforced
54 Biking wear
57 1996 Sandra Bullock film
59 Garfield's best friend
60 Jet-set jet
61 Shaq of basketball
62 Great ___
63 Coat-of-arms border
64 Hollers
65 Spud buds

DOWN

1 Rum cake
2 Jack in *Rio Lobo*
3 1980 Jane Fonda film
4 They aren't widely known
5 Observed
6 Turkish honcho
7 Celtic sea god
8 Deep-___ bend
9 Spielberg and Wright
10 Corporate pirates
11 *Alfred* composer
12 Leo, for one
13 Royal pain
19 High card
21 "Kinda" suffix
25 Shell teams
26 Cartoon skunk
27 Clear kitchen wrap
28 Ewoks' forest moon
29 1996 Michelle Pfeiffer film
30 *The Da Vinci Code* albino
31 Launch
34 Cleric's title: Abbr.
40 Ask
41 Close friend
42 Kellogg's products
43 With ice cream
45 Hang ten
47 MapQuest's owner
50 D-Day campaign town
51 Pitcher
52 Frosty's eyes
53 Unit of force
54 Repair
55 Rake tooth
56 Espies
58 Salt, to a French chef

BRAINSNACK® **Peak Puzzle**

Which number should replace the question mark?

BLOCK ANAGRAM

Form the word that is described in the parentheses, using the letters above the grid. Extra letters are already in the right place.

MERMAID INN (heat wave in autumn)

☐ ☐ ☐ ☐ ☐ ☐ **S** **U** ☐ ☐ ☐

Word Sudoku

Complete the grid so that each row, each column, and each 3 x 3 frame contains the nine letters from the black box below. The hidden nine-letter word is in the diagonal from top left to bottom right.

B D E F I P R S V

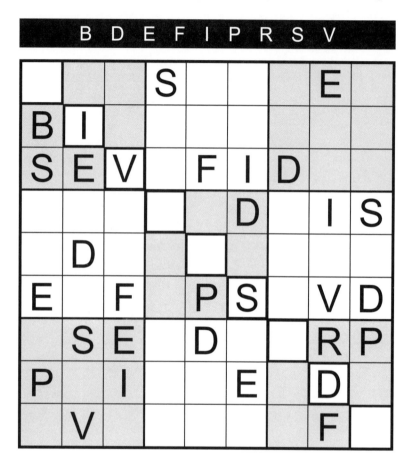

THREE-IN-ONE

Using all of the letters listed below only once, can you find the names of three major rivers of the world?

A A A B E E E G G G I M N N S T Y Z Z Z

TRIVIA QUIZ **Fine Furniture**

Whether you call it a divan, a sofa, or a davenport, the world of fine furnishings
is riddled with interesting facts and details.

1. What type of furniture was originally produced in medieval times to store armor?

   _____

2. American furniture crafted in the Chippendale style was made from about 1750 to 1780 and was named after cabinetmaker Thomas Chippendale's work. Where was Chippendale from?

   _____

3. American furniture crafted in this style dates from the 1720s to about 1750, although the queen it is named after died in 1714. What is it called?

   _____

4. What is an English desk and drawer combination called? (Hint: In America the word came to refer to a chest of drawers generally for the bedroom.)

   _____

5. What do you call a very thin layer of particularly fine wood that has been glued on to inferior wood to produce a smooth and attractive surface?

   _____

6. Why did all of the silver furniture disappear from the royal palaces of France?

   _____

7. What German school of art ushered in a new age of furniture design in 1925?

   _____

8. In China, fine furniture was often made of lacquered wood pieces inlaid with what precious substance?

   _____

9. Duncan Phyfe was a Scottish cabinetmaker but he is know for his work in what country?

   _____

10. What is a credenza?

    _____

11. What is a table with hinges that folds down to half its size called?

    _____

12. What do the numbers mean on anitique furniture?

    _____

Cage the Animals

Draw lines to completely divide up the grid into small squares, with exactly one animal per square. The squares should not overlap.

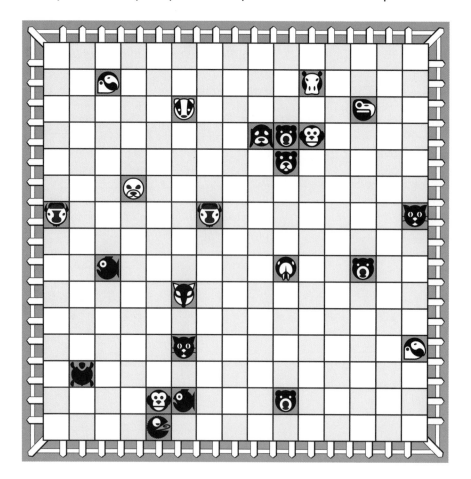

trivia

- Who shot the sheriff in a 1973 song?

68

CROSSWORD '60s Slang

ACROSS

1 Portico in Athens
5 Broom made of twigs
10 Sacred bird of the Nile
14 Young'uns
15 On the double, poetically
16 Skin-colored
17 "Unbelievable!"
19 *Peter Pan* pirate
20 Bitter, as in taste
21 Headed off again
23 Tickled pink
24 Mia Farrow graced its first cover
25 Prepare for winter driving
27 Kindle's Sony rival
30 1975 Wimbledon winner
33 Song finale
35 "Operator" singer
36 Drag wrap
37 Baseless stories
39 Uintah tribe
40 A beatnik beats it
42 Bygone blade
43 A convertiplane
44 Goat or rabbit wool
46 Debaters' focus
48 Bread units
50 Zoologist's object of study
54 Marginal scribbler
56 Hospital attendant
57 Quark site
58 "You got that right, dude!"
60 Soprano Ponselle
61 Induce the jitters
62 Light rope
63 Sharp
64 Moved carefully
65 *Harry Potter* actress Watson

DOWN

1 Northern weasel
2 Kind of typing
3 Relative of 1-Down
4 Sitting on top of
5 Medieval church
6 ___ fail (big blunder)
7 Sink in the middle
8 Form of autumn color
9 Crater maker
10 Parochial
11 Depressed
12 French notion
13 Tennis ranking
18 Sufficiently talented
22 Particulars, for short
24 Nit-pickers
26 Pros and ___
28 Prefix with "plasm"
29 Casting requirement?
30 "Fernando" singers
31 Momentarily
32 Stay calm
34 Word form for "Mars"
37 Yellowish red
38 Left
41 John in *The Big Lebowski*
43 Paleontology, e.g.
45 Not at all eager
47 Subcontinental prefix
49 Nina's mother in *Black Swan*
51 1983 Michael Keaton film
52 Car protector
53 Carter of *Wonder Woman*
54 *The ___ Knight Rises* (2012)
55 Great Plains tribe
56 Czech river
59 Petrol

Binairo

Complete the grid with zeros and ones until there are 5 zeros and 6 ones in every row and every column. No more than two of the same number can be next to or under each other. Rows or columns with exactly the same content are not allowed. There is only one valid solution.

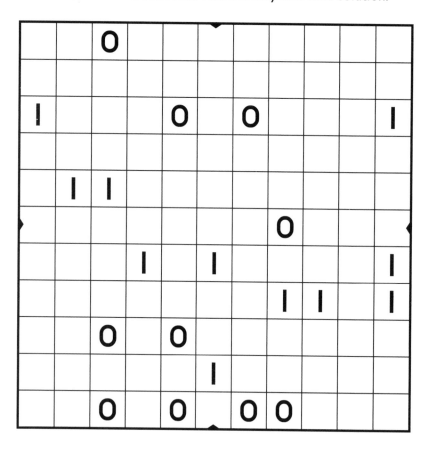

LETTERBLOCKS

Move the letterblocks around so that words associated with imagination are formed on the top and bottom rows. In some blocks the letter from the top row has been switched with the letter from the bottom row.

BRAINSNACK® Sweet Treat

Which plate (1–6) should replace the question mark?

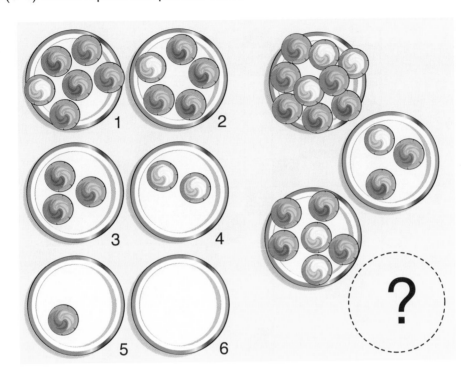

QUICK WORD SEARCH

Find the gems listed below in the word search grid.

G	O	L	D	S	T	O	N	E	T	I	T	K	E	T
S	P	H	E	N	E	P	H	R	I	T	E	D	A	J
Z	A	A	M	E	T	H	Y	S	T	E	N	R	A	G
I	L	N	A	I	D	I	S	B	O	L	Y	R	E	B
M	O	O	N	S	T	O	N	E	T	I	L	L	E	M

**AMETHYST BERYL GARNET GOLDSTONE JADE MELLITE
MOONSTONE NEPHRITE OPAL OBSIDIAN SPHENE TEKTITE**

CROSSWORD ’70s Slang

ACROSS

1 Architect's plinth
5 Indian tea
10 Pop of pop music
14 Cloverleaf feature
15 Exhibited brilliance
16 "Encore!"
17 "I need a favor ..."
19 Petits ___ (peas)
20 Twinkly, in a way
21 Figure wrong
23 Concealed obstacles
24 16th-century Pope
25 ___ good example
27 Tomei in *The Ides of March*
30 Churl
33 Actress Witherspoon
35 Composer Carl Maria von ___
36 Pull
38 Old-fashioned
40 Bruce in *The Cowboys*
41 Miami golf resort
43 Chanteuse Cherry
45 Match the bet
46 Goes "ZZZ" in the night
48 Disinfectant spray
50 Singer Leslie
52 Judge Smails in *Caddyshack*
55 Stoolie
56 Seismograph pickups
58 Award for *Modern Family*
59 "Cool!"
61 Bona fide
62 Privileged few
63 Susan who was Belle
64 Hawaiian goose
65 Marked for exclusion
66 Hall-of-Famer Sandberg

DOWN

1 Dynamic 88, for one
2 Sources
3 Miller salesman
4 La Scala productions
5 Helped
6 Took a picture of
7 Note before la
8 Jungian "self"
9 Sweater size
10 Like drunk drivers
11 Positive feelings
12 Crossword diagram
13 "Be happy to!"
18 *Tattered Tom* author
22 Cabbage salad
24 Easter colors
26 Connery in The Rock
28 Like the Negev
29 "Rule, Britannia!" composer
30 Bookie's quote
31 Elvis ___ Presley
32 "Awesome!"
34 Counting-out word
37 Grotesque waterspout
39 Had coming
42 Plastic block
44 Like Swiss cheese
47 Drooped
49 Supple
51 Haggard of Nashville
53 Grinder
54 Municipal
55 Captain Hook's underling
56 Large bag
57 "Auld Lang ___"
58 East ender
60 Engine additive

WORD SEARCH Nursing

All the words are hidden vertically, horizontally, or diagonally—in both directions. The letters that remain unused form a sentence from left to right.

```
T H E R F R I E N D L Y E M O
T I S G I D E P A R T M E N T
R V R A N A T V H E A L T H I
K O U O N I H O O S A L A R Y
I F O E T H R C E C M W A R D
N E H M L N W Y L R E V E F A
D N G O D I W H S E C R F O M
M E N H T N R W I I E A H L O
P P I R D N W E T T H A O R
S K T I N N E A T S E C W U R
Y B I S I N R I G S I S M A I
C I S N L R Y T T N I G H T U
H R I T E M P E R A T U R E N
I T V B U S Y E O H P E L P D
A H A H O S P I T A L N D A R
T W A S H O S S I C H A N G E
R S T P R S E N I C I D E M S
Y E O T R A I N I N G P L E S
```

- BIRTH
- BUSY
- CALM
- CHANGE
- DEPARTMENT
- DRIP
- ERRATIC
- FEVER
- FRIENDLY
- HEALTH
- HOME
- HOSPITAL
- KIND
- MEDICINES
- NIGHT
- PATIENT
- PSYCHIATRY
- RECOVER
- REPORT
- ROOM
- SALARY
- STAFF
- STERILE
- SYRINGE
- TEMPERATURE
- TRAINING
- UNDRESS
- VISITING HOURS
- WARD
- WASH
- WHEELCHAIR
- WHITE

Word Wheel

How many words of three or more letters, each including the letter at the center of the wheel, can you make from this diagram? No plurals or conjugations. We've found 17, including one nine-letter word. Can you do better?

SANDWICH

What five-letter word belongs between the word at left and the word at right, so that the first and second word, and the second and third word, each form a common compound word or phrase?

EYES _ _ _ _ _ LINE

CROSSWORD **Queens**

ACROSS

1 Hawaiian coffee
5 "___ on a true story"
10 Brown-and-white porgy
14 Luise Rainer role in *The Good Earth*
15 Benedict XVI's cape
16 Prefix meaning "one trillion"
17 Queen of Country
19 Conductor Gilbert
20 The tiniest bit
21 Incumbent
23 MADD focus
24 Guide strap
25 Ousted
29 General idea
32 Put in high spirits
33 Classical east wind
35 Anti-narcotics org.
36 Wax-glazed fabric
37 *Rescue Me* actor Leary
38 Toothpaste flavor
39 "___ Time at All": Beatles
40 Hospital employees
41 *Shrek* princess
42 Slumber party attire
44 Pale lager
46 Floating jail
47 "Hardly!"
48 Whales are high ones
51 Hailing from Haifa
55 Four Tops member Benson
56 Queen of R&B
58 Convey via Ameslan
59 *Amadeus* director Forman
60 Morlock prey
61 1992 Derby winner Lil ___
62 Gone
63 Tax form data: Abbr.

DOWN

1 *The Mikado* executioner
2 Lena in *Chocolat*
3 Thurmond of basketball
4 Remedy
5 Chevrolet logo
6 Field
7 "Erie Canal" mule
8 Pipe bends
9 Wishing for
10 Noisy opposition
11 Queen of Pop
12 Monitor lizard
13 Hunger sign
18 "After ___ Gone" (jazz standard)
22 30 make 300
25 Postgame report
26 *Nadja* actress Lowensohn
27 Queen of Hip Hop
28 Title documents
29 Like a potato chip
30 Slant-cut pasta
31 13th-century invader
34 One for Jacques
37 Blueprints
38 Boo-boos
40 Gaston's gal
41 Lady's-slipper and baby's-breath
43 Francis of *What's My Line*
45 Be emphatic
48 Pink drink
49 Passing notice
50 Space for a ship
51 Living legend
52 Sinuous shockers
53 *Lolita* star Sue
54 Goddess with a cow's head
57 Quebec island

Sudoku

Fill in the grid so that each row, each column, and each 3 x 3 frame contains every number from 1 to 9.

	8		6	9	3		2	
2		9	4		5			6
6	3	4	8		1	9	7	
								2
		8	9		7		1	
	7				8			3
		7			9		4	
5		2						

SYMBOL SUMS

Can you work out these number sums using three of these four symbols? $+ \ - \ \div \ \times$

$$24 \ \square \ 25 \ \square \ 1 \ \square \ 8 = 6$$

Whorls

Which is the odd one out?

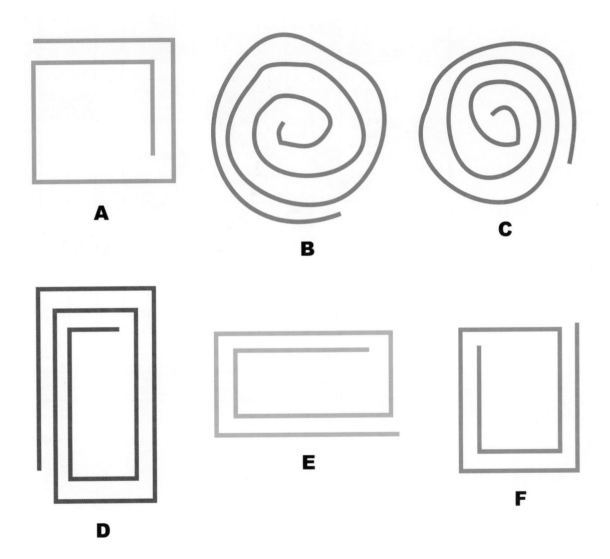

CROSSWORD Themeless 3

ACROSS

1 Police unit
5 Weasel look-alike
10 FBI operatives
14 What a stitch in time saves
15 *Midnight in Paris* director
16 Exuberant review
17 Took turns
19 Brain wave
20 Sun orbiters
21 Tangerine section
23 Antipasto meat
24 Uzbekistan sea
25 Stick with a prod
27 Way of doing things
30 Harvest-ready
33 Cogwheel
35 Camouflages
36 Suffix for Capri
37 *Road to Rio* star
39 Louse egg
40 "___ Eclipse of the Heart"
42 West Point rival: Abbr.
43 Citi Field team
44 Dishonest
46 Caesar's last words
48 Ancient route
49 Methodology
53 Wisconsin capital
56 It's scanned at checkout
57 First Olympic site
58 Light red table wine
60 *The Sound of Music* baroness
61 Old newsboy's call
62 Some annexes
63 *Young Frankenstein* actress
64 Bundle bearer
65 Loom reed

DOWN

1 Finger clicks
2 *O Pioneers!* author Cather
3 Conductor Dorati
4 Juvenile
5 Capital of Chile
6 Cry of grief
7 Pork sandwich
8 Dregs
9 Evoke affection
10 Pained look
11 Stowe in *Blink*
12 Level
13 Spruce
18 San ___ (Riviera resort)
22 Orchard
26 Unveiling
27 Accident-___
28 Buttonhole
29 Russia called them TU-144s
30 Campus cadet org.
31 Myself included
32 Lab glass
34 Massage reactions
37 B.B. King's music
38 Vanna White's costar
41 Craftsman
43 Mr. Universe's pride
45 Investigates
47 Inexperienced one
50 "... and ___ a good-night!"
51 Circus Maximus official
52 Cluttered
53 Lamblike
54 Pasta ___ Carbonara
55 Barber shop call
56 Jefferson's vice president
59 From ___ Z (totally)

BRAINSNACK® **Alphablock**

Which letterblock should replace the question mark?

CROSSWORD Kings

ACROSS

1 Sporting
5 Danes in *The Rainmaker*
11 Type of quiz
14 Actor Auberjonois
15 Set
16 Baboon
17 King of Soul
19 Dog's doc
20 Cute cats
21 Frankfurters
23 Blender options
24 *Mr. Mom* star Teri
25 Castillian kings
27 Brit rescuer
30 Orals, e.g.
33 News to a baseball player
35 Chinese restaurant general
36 *Gladiator* composer Zimmer
37 Shiny shell lining
38 Bingo call
39 GI recreation provider
40 Beethoven's ___ *Solemnis*
41 Exodus plague
42 Breadbasket
44 Cherubic topper
46 Rose shade
47 Phylicia of *The Cosby Show*
51 Curbside water source
54 Chum
55 "___-hoo!"
56 King of Country
58 Made a ditch
59 Chef Lagasse
60 Somme srta.
61 Bit of work
62 Sully
63 Stone

DOWN

1 Sites of mysterious circles
2 Subside
3 Biscotto flavoring
4 Trifles, e.g.
5 Like nachos
6 Little boys
7 Suffix for drunk
8 "Got it, daddy-o!"
9 Defector
10 Personalize a bracelet, e.g.
11 King of the High C's
12 Shop sign
13 Vet charges?
18 Takes a backseat
22 Medical scan
26 Hide away
27 "Winter Song" singer McLachlan
28 One being exploited
29 Jockey Turcotte et al.
30 That being so
31 It's right on the map
32 King of Rap
34 Some colas
37 Bubba or Slim, e.g.
38 Flowers
40 Got by
41 Panache
43 Early space station
45 Capable of cultivation
48 Hawaiian outlander
49 Tibia neighbor
50 Treated with tablets
51 Chicago park
52 BYOB portion
53 Like bacon
54 Golfer Mickelson
57 ___-color pasta

Do the Math

Enter numbers in each row and column to arrive at the end totals.
Only numbers 1–9 are used and only once.

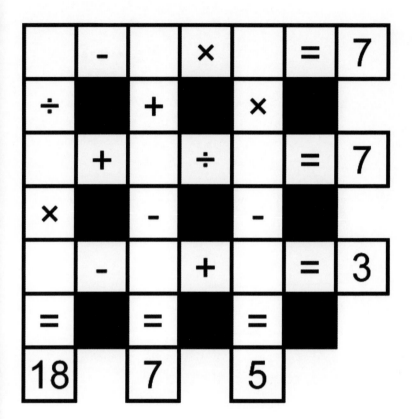

trivia

- Who played Virgil Tibbs in *In the Heat of the Night*?

Word Pyramid

Each word in the pyramid has the letters of the word above it, plus a new letter.

B
(1) exist
(2) place to sleep
(3) liability
(4) introduction
(5) broken
(6) slowest
(7) tripped

do you **KNOW**?

What is a triangle with no equal sides called?

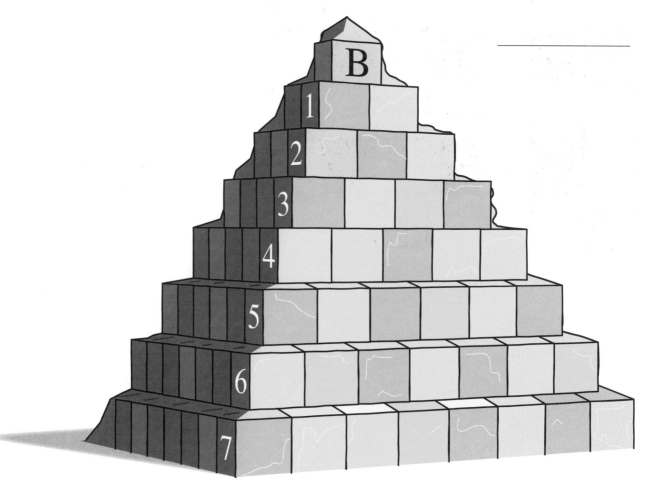

Sudoku

Fill in the grid so that each row, each column, and each 3 x 3 frame contains every number from 1 to 9.

6		9			3			2
	5	9				3	1	4
4			1	2		7	6	
3	5			1				
		3					9	7
7		2	8	6	4	3		
	2				7		4	
		8	3		9			

trivia

- Who wrote the Beatles' song "And I Love Her"?

_____

SYMBOL SUMS

Can you work out these number sums using three of these four symbols? $+$ $-$ $\div$ $\times$

$$3 \ \square \ 56 \ \square \ 3 \ \square \ 3 = 55$$

Atomic Numbers

ACROSS

1 Scott Joplin numbers
5 Does a bartender's job
10 Eyelid problem
14 *The Lord of the Rings* monster
15 Group of wives
16 Not in residence
17 Bromine's atomic number
19 Billy Budd's captain
20 Get out the vote
21 Leaves on base
23 "Rumble in the Jungle" victor
24 "___ Misbehavin'"
25 Link up
29 Assumed names
32 Finished parasailing
33 Carnival music
35 ___ *Good Men* (1992)
36 Grappling win
37 Fruit-filled dessert
38 Guadalajara goose
39 Holiday kickoffs
41 Caesar ____
43 It brings a tear to the eye
44 Hates to the max
46 B'nai B'rith symbol
48 Once around Sol
49 Deep
50 Camera protector
53 Grief
57 *The Kite Runner* narrator
58 Silver's atomic number
60 Larch relative
61 *Shark Tale* jellyfish
62 *Green Mansions* girl
63 Addressed the court
64 First Super Bowl MVP
65 Banana peel mishap

DOWN

1 Campus mil. group
2 Turkish high official
3 Partner of bear it
4 Estate employee
5 Popular science
6 Bumblers
7 Canton of Altdorf
8 Gets ready to drag
9 *The Bartered Bride* composer
10 Gazelle's habitat
11 Chromium's atomic number
12 Doghouse locale
13 "Smoke Gets in Your ___"
18 It may be hard to believe
22 2011 animated film
25 Dressed like Superman
26 Source of oil
27 Einsteinium's atomic number
28 Malaga munchies
29 From port to starboard
30 Hajj destination
31 Mower's path
34 Wire measure
40 Becomes irate
41 Rakes with gunfire
42 Procrastinator
43 Bummers
45 Anatomical pouch
47 Christie's bids
50 Arctic reindeer herder
51 Marathoner Zatopek
52 Sweet wine
53 Rouse to action
54 Diabolic
55 Big rig
56 Go off the deep end
59 Messenger molecule

Futoshiki

Fill in the 5 x 5 grid with the numbers from 1 to 5 once per row and column, while following the greater-than/lesser-than symbols shown. There is only one valid solution that can be reached through logic and clear thinking alone!

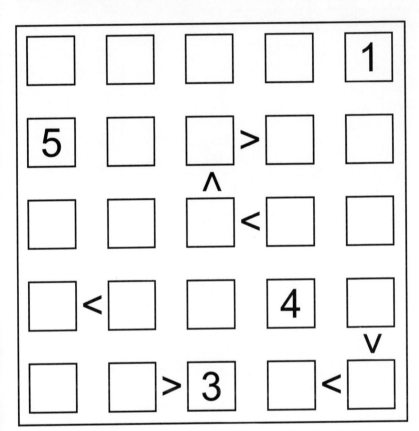

do you KNOW?

What is the tallest mountain in the solar system?

_____

TRIANAGRAM

Three-word groups of anagrams are also called triplets or trianagrams.
Complete the group:

P A R T S _ _ _ _ _   _ _ _ _ _

Corrections

Which two numbers should be erased in order to restore the logic of the series of numbers?

WORD WALL

Beginning at the left side of the wall, make a word by adding one group of letters from each column as you move left to right. When you have found the first word, go back to the second column and start the next word, gathering one group of letters from each column and so on until all the letters are used to make six words.

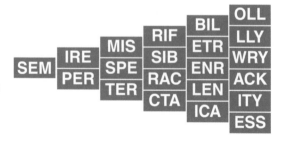

CROSSWORD Famous Firsts

ACROSS

1 CFO degrees
5 Makes a mistake
10 *The Kite Runner* narrator
14 Witherspoon in *Dark Victory*
15 Jekyll's servant
16 *A Cat in Paris* cat
17 He was on the first cover of *Rolling Stone*
19 Store
20 What Demosthenes practiced
21 Oregon time
23 Bluish white twinklers
24 Japanese for "tiger"
25 Admission costs
27 G.W. Bush's first Supreme Court nominee
30 Pulled in
33 Missouri or Colorado
35 Word with kettle or steel
36 Ending with pay or plug
37 ___ chi chu'an
38 Wife of 17-Across
39 Folk singer Ives
41 Hierarchy levels
43 Draped drapery
44 Sunning choices
46 Sweet 16 org.
48 Goggle-eye fish
49 Commotion
53 "Maybe yes, maybe no"
56 Genesis garden snake
57 "Groove ___ the Heart": Deee-Lite
58 Poland's first non-Communist president
60 Victuals
61 Eventuate
62 Knievel of stunts
63 Jumbo, say
64 It's taken by witnesses
65 Drier than dry

DOWN

1 Low-level position
2 Coarse ones
3 Nirvana attainer
4 New Mexico capital
5 The Faerie Queene poet
6 Dragged out
7 Free electron
8 Go kerplunk
9 Lawmaker
10 Thought much of
11 She was on the first cover of *People*
12 Crucifix letters
13 Campus cadet org.
18 Old Roman coins
22 Corn holder
26 Position
27 Royal rule
28 Salad fish
29 Weather word
30 Actor Lee J. ___
31 His, in Paris
32 First athlete to win seven Olympic gold medals
34 SUV kin
40 A photo ID
41 Verbal puzzles
42 Exploited, slangily
43 Tastes
45 Woods of *China Beach*
47 Mystique
50 Grievance
51 Four-time Indy champ Al
52 Like knock-knock jokes
53 Conks out
54 Morales of *NYPD Blue*
55 In the mail
56 Give the cold shoulder to
59 Johnny Reb's org.

Classical Capers

If you know classical music, you'll waltz through these!

1. Who composed the opera Don Giovanni?
   a. Beethoven
   b. J. S. Bach
   c. Leonard Bernstein
   d. Mozart

2. How is Dvorak's Symphony No. 9 better known?
   a. The "New World Symphony"
   b. "The Wedding March"
   c. The Lone Ranger theme song

3. Who composed the classical music on which the pop song "A Whiter Shade of Pale" was based?
   a. Puccini
   b. J. S. Bach
   c. Tchaikovsky

4. The Duke of Mantua is a character in which opera?
   a. *The Pirates of Penzance*
   b. *Die Fledermaus*
   c. *Rigoletto*

5. Which opera is set aboard the HMS *Indomitable*?
   a. *Billy Budd*
   b. *Mutiny on the Bounty*
   c. *The Pirates of Penzance*

6. Who composed the *Peer Gynt Suites*?
   a. Edvard Grieg
   b. Jacob de Haan
   c. Cornelius Dopper

7. What is the title of Beethoven's only opera?
   a. *Cosi fan Tutte*
   b. *The Marriage of Figaro*
   c. *Fidelio*

8. Who composed "The Blue Danube Waltz"?
   a. Johann Strauss
   b. J. S. Bach
   c. Frederic Chopin

9. What is the alternative name for Bach's Air from Suite No. 3?
   a. "Air on a G String"
   b. "Afternoon Etude"
   c. "Amsterdam Air"

10. What does the musical direction rallentando signify?
    a. Play slurs between the notes indicated
    b. Suddenly play very fast
    c. Slow the music

trivia

- How many types of waltz are there?

WORD SEARCH Jurisprudence

All the words are hidden vertically, horizontally, or diagonally—in both directions. The letters that remain unused form a sentence from left to right.

```
T R I A L J C U R E I B I L L
S P R A D L U D E D F I N E N
C C G H A E T O E O I S A A I
L O L I C R F O R C F T H C N
T E M J O E T E U D D I C Q D
I S A P S Y E R N L E D E U I
T C E L L U N P E D I R S I C
E R L E I A S O S P A O N T T
C N E A C C I P L S X N M T M
H A T D R D A N E E O E T A E
N T T E I B Y S T C F C O L N
I S E U M R T Y E S T O F L T
C E R A E L T N P A D V I C E
A T S W I L T R D O S S I E R
L N A V I N O D J U S T I C E
I O I U T O B J E C T I O N J
T C G R F I B U L E S N U O C
Y N A P R O C E D U R E B L S
```

- ACQUITTAL
- ADVICE
- BILL
- CASE
- CIVIL
- CLAIMS
- CODE
- COMPLAINT
- CONTEST
- COUNSEL
- CRIME
- DEFENDANT
- DOSSIER
- EXPERT
- FELONY
- FINE
- GUILTY
- INDICTMENT
- INNOCENT
- JOB
- JUSTICE
- LETTERS
- OBJECTION
- ORDER
- PLEAD
- PROCEDURE
- PROOF
- REPORT
- SPEECH
- SUSPECT
- TECHNICALITY
- TOGA
- TRIAL

Sport Maze

Draw the shortest way from the ball to the goal. You can only move along vertical and horizontal lines, not along diagonal lines. The figure on each square indicates the number of squares the ball must move in the same direction. You can change direction at each stop.

1	1	2	1	5	0
2	4	4	4	4	2
1	3	3	2	3	5
2	1	1	0	●	1
1	1	2	1	4	4
1	1	2	2	3	1

trivia

- Who coined the word "chortle"?

ONE LETTER LESS OR MORE

The word on the right side contains the letters of the word on the left side, plus or minus the letter in the middle. One letter is already in the right place.

S O U V E N I R -I ☐ ☐ ☐ V ☐ ☐ ☐

CROSSWORD · Their Final Films 1

ACROSS

1 They're caught in pots
5 Long-legged bird
10 *Law & Order: SVU* star
14 Betazoid on the *Enterprise*
15 Boss, often
16 Andy Kaufman series
17 *On Golden Pond* was his final film
19 Like the Sinai
20 Rain forest felines
21 Clerical assistant
23 Walked boldly
24 Branch of math
25 Fleming and McEwan
27 Jason in *Magnolia*
30 Rustic structure
33 Take a vow
35 Japan's first capital
36 ___ shoestring (cheaply)
37 Jeremy's *Entourage* role
38 Geometric fastener
39 Cross to bear
41 Salt Lake City's "ESA" is one
43 S&L services
44 McDowell in *Caligula*
46 Little falling-out
48 Bad "Monopoly" space
49 *Red Tails* roles
53 Storm sound
56 ...Élan
57 Retained
58 *Avalanche Express* was his final film
60 Renata Scotto solo
61 False cover
62 Donegal Bay feeder
63 Start of a game
64 1983 Amy Irving film
65 Future flower

DOWN

1 Bottled water brand
2 At attention
3 Aloof one
4 Prime cut
5 Relents
6 Uncommon dice rolls
7 Pay-to-stay place
8 Helen of Troy's mother
9 It has a lot of pull
10 Venetian language
11 *Walk, Don't Run* was his final film
12 Glowing theater sign
13 It may go out at night
18 Luke Skywalker's teacher
22 Crystal ball, for example
26 Body of bees
27 Spoils a parade
28 Buddy Rich's instrument
29 High school tests
30 Explosive sound
31 Ballet star Pavlova
32 *Street Fighter* was his final film
34 Poet's "prior to"
40 *National Enquirer* fodder
41 Reason for a rash response?
42 Raiment
43 Travel guides
45 Suffix for planet
47 "___ We Got Fun?"
50 Earthy pigment
51 Title for Macbeth
52 Was a seamstress
53 Jazz trumpeter Jones
54 "Try some!"
55 Debauchee
56 Buda's 1873 merger partner
59 Coffer

Kakuro

Each number in a black area is the sum of the numbers that you have to enter in the next empty boxes. The empty boxes that make up the sum are called a run. The sum of the across run is written above the diagonal in the black area, and the sum of the down run is written below the diagonal. Runs can only contain the numbers 1 through 9, and each number in a run can only be used once. The gray boxes only contain odd numbers and the white only even numbers.

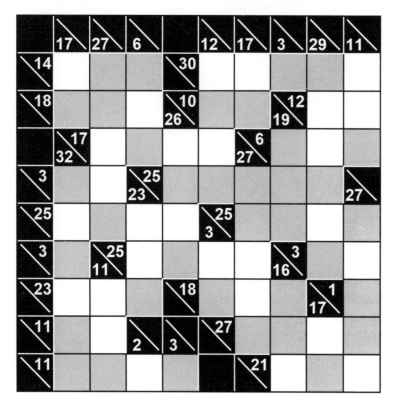

SANDWICH

What five-letter word belongs between the word at left and the word at right, so that the first and second word, and the second and third word, each form a common compound word or phrase?

W I N T E R _ _ _ _ _ **H O U S E**

Sudoku X

Fill in the grid so that each row, each column, and each 3 x 3 frame contains every number from 1 to 9. The two main diagonals of the grid also contain every number from 1 to 9.

			4	6				
					5	1	8
4								
6	2		3	9				
	5	9	6					
2	3						7	6
7	9		6	8	4			
1	6	4	2		8	3		

do you KNOW?

The word "plumber" comes from which metal?

BLOCK ANAGRAM

Form the word that is described in the parentheses, using the letters above the grid. Extra letters are already in the right place.

HOT WATER (boundary separating two masses of air)

	E				R		F		N	

Their Final Films 2

ACROSS

1 Spreadsheet filler
5 Cilic of tennis
10 Sail support
14 Spirited style
15 "Set Fire to the Rain" singer
16 ___ Domini
17 *Wicked Stepmother* was her final film
19 Angry dog sound
20 Lattice
21 Give it a go
23 Bridge builder's concern
24 Anderson in *Stranded*
25 Antique autos
27 Ma and Pa of film
30 Alter egos
33 Nymph of myth
35 Aged Hamburger?
36 "Either it goes ___ do!"
37 Sharapova shot
38 Deer in *Bambi*
39 Primordial material
41 Hacienda honorific
43 Study like crazy
44 Houlihan of *M*A*S*H*
46 "The Vamp" of silents
48 Of aircraft
49 Hardly cheery
53 Compensation
56 Without hypocrisy
57 Heraldic charge
58 *Two-Faced Woman* was her final film
60 North Carolina campus
61 Prop for Emily Carr
62 "Runaround Sue" singer
63 Metzger in *Murder, She Wrote*
64 Jaguar markings
65 French auxiliary verb

DOWN

1 Card balances
2 It's high when it's red
3 Home run, in slang
4 Buck features
5 *Splash* mermaid
6 Lovelace and Rehan
7 New Testament book: Abbr.
8 Figure skater Kulik
9 Got cozy
10 Four-color printing ink
11 *Mulholland Drive* was her final film
12 Lose control
13 Cause for a lawsuit
18 "You're something ___!"
22 Little shaver
26 Garage activities
27 Food on a skewer
28 Volcano near Messina
29 Coal stratum
30 Cry of disdain
31 Buck add-on
32 *These Old Broads* was her final film
34 Accelerator particle
40 Oxygen, for one
41 Bath needs
42 Some are steel-belted
43 Waterfall
45 Anger
47 Bout site
50 Rate
51 Grapevine support
52 Sierra ___
53 Elegy, for one
54 Folk singer Guthrie
55 Mouse hazard
56 Galley notation
59 Paul Anka's "___ Beso"

BRAINSNACK® Under Your Skin

Which skin cell (1–6) should replace the question mark?

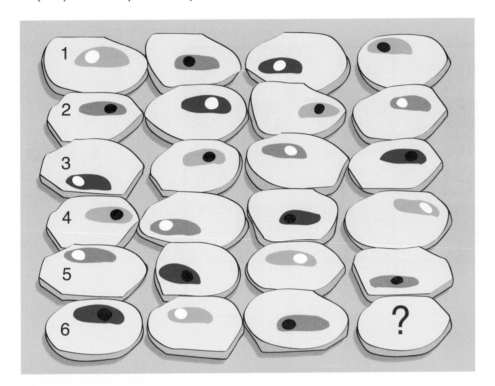

QUICK CROSSWORD

Place the cooking terms listed below in the crossword grid.

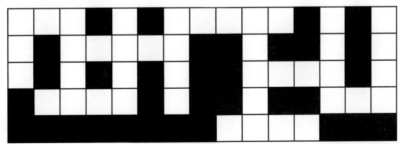

AIOLI BEAT COAT DICE DIP DRUPE DRY PARE
PASTA PATE RACK SAKE STEW WOK

Do the Math

Enter numbers in each row and column to arrive at the end totals.
Numbers must be from 1 to 9 and used only once.

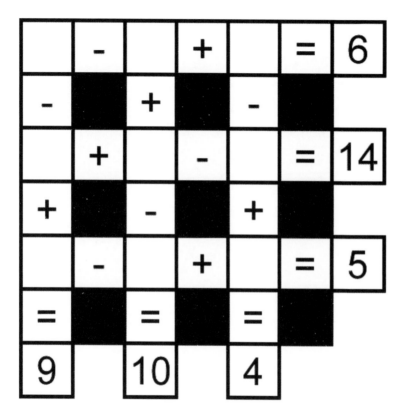

trivia

- Who wrote the novel *The Godfather?*

CROSSWORD Long-Running Musicals

ACROSS

1 Strand of smoke
5 Succumbs to wanderlust
10 Unwelcome e-mail
14 Spot
15 God of the Koran
16 Texas city south of Dallas
17 Leonine retreat
18 "I Will Be" singer Lewis
19 Cologne coin
20 "I Am What I Am" musical
23 Shrimp dish
24 ___ Morgana (mirage)
25 *Othello* role
27 Flaws
30 "The Alphabet Song" beginning
33 Baseball dinger
35 Culkin in "Twelve"
36 Liverpool lav
37 Sharp turn
38 Chaney of old horror flicks
39 1958 Elvis Presley hit
41 Daughter of Lear
43 Pay honor to
44 Google's smartphone OS
46 Motown music category
48 Be on the payroll
49 Simple sweepers
53 "Anything You Can Do" musical
58 Where some signs change
59 Like Wrigley Field's walls
60 Rick's girl in Paris
61 *The ___ of March* (2011)
62 Twit
63 Like Lake Tanganyika
64 "___ Dinah": Frankie Avalon
65 Tallboy
66 Does simple arithmetic

DOWN

1 The *War of the Worlds* author
2 Father of Jacob
3 Type of bandage
4 Louvre Museum entrance
5 N. Carolina's "City of Oaks"
6 Olive, to Ovid
7 Ballplayer Moises
8 Cat without a tail
9 *Amadeus* playwright
10 Feel the heat
11 "Me" singer
12 Hell's half-___
13 Holstein hellos
21 2.5, e.g.
22 Awkward one
26 Ran thickly
27 "The Ballet Class" painter
28 Gait slower than a canter
29 "... for auld lang ___"
30 Robert in *Guys and Dolls* (1950)
31 Welcome benefit
32 Like dew
34 Wheel type
40 Walk aimlessly
41 Like some phone endorsements?
42 "___ Perfect": Miley Cyrus
43 Gainesville locale
45 Find that's mined
47 Mufasa's mother
50 Eyed amorously
51 Contemplated
52 Wigs out
53 Vitamin C, e.g.
54 Like naturists
55 Nefarious
56 Cohen-Chang on *Glee*
57 Longings

Letter Soup

Use up all the letters in the soup to fill in the spaces and find eight sailing terms.

ANC _ O _	_ AT _ R
_ _ CHT	_ E _ AT _ A
C _ M _ A _ S	_ OO _
_ ATA _ ARA _	A _ T _ R EC _

Sudoku Twin

Fill in the grid so that each row, each column, and each 3 x 3 frame contains every number from 1 to 9. A sudoku twin is two connected 9 x 9 sudokus.

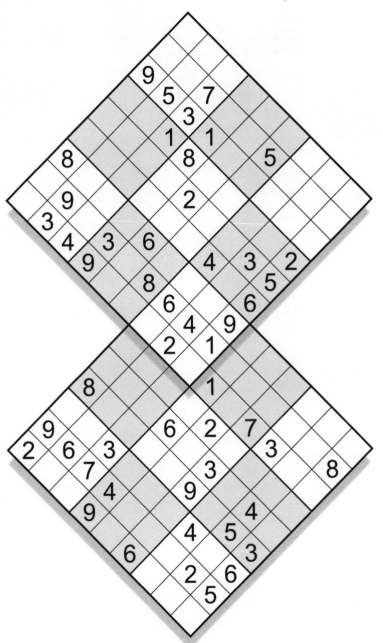

delete ONE

Delete one letter from

PARANOIA TO LIE

and rearrange the rest to find something to listen to.

_____

Secret Garden

ACROSS

1 Refuge for strays
5 Summer Triangle star
10 Footless creature
14 Horse for Lawrence
15 Mother's mother, e.g.
16 Fish, to an osprey
17 Kissers
18 ___ and shaker
19 Chaplin of *Game of Thrones*
20 In a moody way
22 Grappling hold
24 Noah's debarkation site
25 Not being used
26 Totally bungled
28 Settle a dispute
31 Hatteras or Canaveral
34 Flowers hidden in clue answers
36 "Be happy to!"
37 Hog fat
38 One of a cartoon duo
39 Aerobic bit
40 Conquistador's cache
41 Built-out window
43 Houston hockey pro
44 It's bound to happen
47 Durability
49 Put-in-Bay's lake
50 Early computer
54 Most polite
56 Lamp fuel
58 Jack-in-the-pulpit
59 Bury in a ceremonial vase
61 1977 whale film
62 Quash
63 Telegraph pioneer
64 Glum drop
65 Czech river
66 Door sign
67 Herpetorium hissers

DOWN

1 Hayek in *Ask the Dust*
2 Previous arrest
3 *It's a Wonderful Life* director
4 Took in
5 Harvest goddess
6 Organic compound
7 Dark blue
8 Hot time in Provence
9 *Weekend at ___* (1989)
10 God of light
11 New convert
12 Wine prefix
13 Cannon in *Caddyshack II*
21 "Low Bridge" mule
23 Sullivan and Wynn
27 Distress
28 Ask for more *Time*
29 Zig or zag
30 Nickname of a Bruin legend
31 Lump of dirt
32 River through Lake Thun
33 Take to court
35 Sardine whale
39 Resort near Tampa
41 Quondam
42 Apprentice
45 Aftershock
46 ___ *for Innocent*: Grafton
48 Blood-group system
51 Roman grain goddess
52 Open a well
53 Kmart merger partner
54 *Avatar* humanoids
55 Wraths
56 Conductor Masur
57 Scots Gaelic
60 *Sine qua___*

BRAINSNACK® # Christmas Lights

Which Christmas tree (1–6) is lit up incorrectly?

CLOCKWISE

The answers to the clues from 1 to 12 are all seven-letter words that end with the letter Y. When you have solved the puzzle correctly, working clockwise from 1, the 12 letters in the outer circle will spell a a word that leaves you on edge.

1 Slander
2 Church's public service
3 Early stages
4 Power of the mind
5 Invalid reasoning
6 Agreement, accord
7 Archaic pseudoscience
8 Posy
9 Seriousness, importance
10 Exalted feeling, rapture
11 To correct
12 Unformed, undetailed

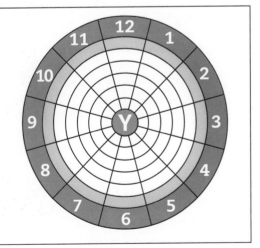

Hourglass

Starting in the middle, each word in the top half has the letters of the word below it, plus a new letter, and each word in the bottom half has the letters of the word above it, plus a new letter.

(1) Freak

(2) Trusted counselor

(3) Subway

(4) To a greater extent

(5) Arab ruler

(6) Criminal offense

(7) Based on the meter as a unit

(8) Associated with heat

WORD SEARCH Machines

All the words are hidden vertically, horizontally, or diagonally—in both directions. The letters that remain unused form a sentence from left to right.

```
A M T E N S I O N S P R I N G
A C R E K A H S H I N R E I S
D U S R E T E M G N I K R A P
E U A L L E N D O S C O P E H
F Y A T Y P E O S F E L E C O
I R E G N A H C X E T A E H T
B N R E T N A L C I G A M B O
R T P R C N B E O N I C I E C
I E N M N A O U B S T R U L O
L X M E A I R B R U S H E L P
L T R N T L U D R N T S E O I
A R D T O P N E R U E Y R W E
T U F O R M A U S E T R A S R
O D I S P L A Y S P A N E R C
R E C O R D E R I F I D I C X
T R E N O H P E L E T A E W S
R E S S E R D L E E H W K R T
G N I N O I T I D N O C R I A
```

- AIR CONDITIONING
- AIRBRUSH
- BELLOWS
- BURNER
- CARD READER
- DEFIBRILLATOR
- DISPLAY
- ENDOSCOPE
- EXTRUDER
- HEAT EXCHANGER
- IRIS SCANNER
- MAGIC LANTERN
- PARKING METER
- PHOTOCOPIER
- RECORDER
- SHAKER
- SUN LAMP
- TELEPHONE
- TENSION SPRING
- TWIN-TURBO
- WHEEL DRESSER
- X-RAY TUBE

Beat the Heat

ACROSS

1 Jai ___ (sport)
5 Fast as you can
9 King Kong was one
12 Type of pear
13 Rocket specialists
14 Actress Farrow
15 "For goodness' ___"
16 Take a dip in the ___ pool
18 Summertime buzzers
20 Glue
21 Write sloppily
24 Indicator
25 Furious
26 ___ conditioning
27 Story of Zeus
28 Create a breeze with a paper ___
29 Pope from 1939-'58
33 Beat the heat with refreshing iced ___
34 Inferno author
35 Stick (to)
39 Band instrument
40 Cease-fire
41 Killer whale
42 Stay chill with this summertime treat
44 Greenish hue
48 Hot ___ furnace (2 words)
49 Soybeans or corn
50 Shrek, for example
51 9-digit ID
52 Word on a map at the mall
53 Onionlike vegetable

DOWN

1 Tummy muscles
2 Mauna ___ volcano
3 Pose a question
4 Cools you down fast (2 words.)
5 Famous photographer Adams
6 Cuts down a tree
7 "___ live and breathe" (2 words)
8 Baby
9 Wrong
10 Type of bean
11 Excited
17 The Old ___ and the Sea
19 Lamb's mama
21 Card used in phones
22 Show sadness
23 Templeton from *Charlotte's Web*
24 Murder, for example
26 Organization for drivers
28 Entry cost
29 Umbrella for the sun
30 B&B
31 Native Americans from the Great Basin area
32 Complete group
33 Long coat with a belt
34 "What's up, ___?"
35 Rand McNally book
36 Prom gown
37 Word before nature or being
38 Prefix meaning "environment"
39 Paper used in decoration
41 Unpleasant smell
43 "My lips ___ sealed"
45 The ___ of Innocence
46 Advanced test
47 Word screamed at the sight of a mouse

Surveillance!

Enter the maze, pass over all security cameras from behind (thereby disabling them) and then exit. You may not pass through a grid space more than once, and may not enter a grid space in the line of a camera you have not disabled.

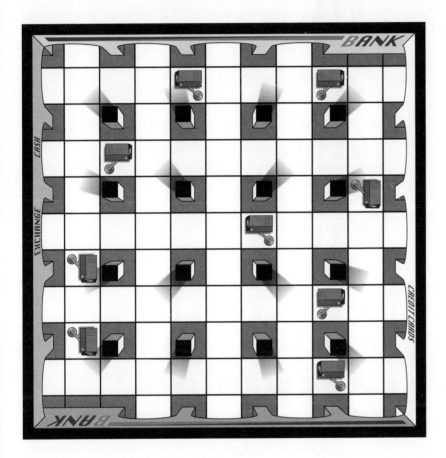

do you KNOW?

What is the target score in blackjack?

FRIENDS

What do the following words have in common?

BANGLE DINGHY JUGGERNAUT LOOT SHAMPOO THUG

Word Parts

Place the left and right word parts with the middle letters to form six new words.

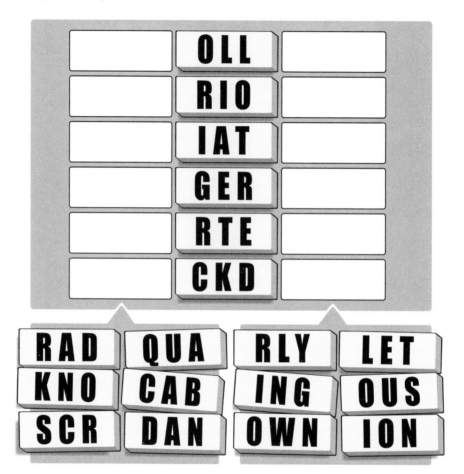

SANDWICH

What three-letter word belongs between the word at left and the word at right, so that the first and second word, and the second and third word, each form a common compound word or phrase?

FALL _ _ _ CROP

CROSSWORD One Way

ACROSS

1 Start of a step quote
5 Verge on
9 Departed
13 Hillside shelter
14 Xenocrates' mentor
15 Endoscopic focuses
16 Settings for some high rollers
17 Mist
18 Striker's score
19 Steamed Mexican treat
21 Mandalay Bay dancer
23 Psychic
25 Hybrid aircraft
26 Step quote: Part 3
28 Calisthenics stance
32 Sporty Saturn
35 Sonata movements
37 Christmas carol
38 S&L transactions
40 HMS, American-style
41 Eyed greedily
42 Incantation word
43 Respiratory woe
45 SAT org.
46 Classified listing
48 End of step quote
50 Shield boss
52 Penguin species
55 Thaw
59 Naval task force
61 Prefix for chute
62 *Bolero* composer
64 Irradiate
65 Kiwi-shaped
66 Minnesota team
67 Start of a plea
68 Brooklyn cagers
69 Shopper stopper
70 Author of step quote: Part 2

DOWN

1 Shoemaker's form
2 Girder
3 Lens holder
4 Step quote: Part 2
5 Swiss peak
6 Carrie Nation targets
7 Western Indians
8 Camry and Corolla
9 Eel-like
10 Weena, for one
11 Approach
12 Like the Tokyo Skytree
14 "Fake" prefix
20 They speak with forked tongues
22 Stir-fry pan
24 Some are pull-down
27 Step quote: Part 4
29 Birthmark
30 Borscht ingredient
31 Alero, for one
32 Close noisily
33 Bryant of the NBA
34 Loom need
36 Milo in *Ulysses*
39 Come-out rolls of 7 and 11
41 Sagebrusher
43 Brooks and Finney
44 Some are silver
47 French soul
49 Author of step quote: Part 1
51 Conductor Seiji
53 "Are you hurt?" response
54 Official under Caesar
55 Informed about
56 Basilica area
57 *Animal House* house
58 Knavish
60 Like ___ of bricks
63 LAX-JFK flight path

Lost in Translation

Word meanings often get lost or forgotten when words travel across borders.
Can you help recover their lost baggage?

1. What is the literal meaning of the name Nova Scotia?

   a. New Scotland
   b. New Scooter
   c. Scottish Hatchback
   d. Scottish Star

2. What does the name Sierra Leone mean in Spanish?

   a. Desert Lions
   b. Stormy Desert
   c. Lion Mountains
   d. Long Coast

3. Which island's name means "rich port" when translated?

   a. Madagascar
   b. Puerto Rico
   c. Barbados
   d. Singapore

4. Which Central American country's name incorporates the Spanish word for water?

   a. Honduras
   b. El Salvador
   c. Panama
   d. Nicaragua

5. Which one of the following countries' names derives from the Phoenician word for *refuge*?

   a. Malta
   b. Italy
   c. Belgium
   d. New Zealand

6. Which European country's name means "eastern kingdom"?

   a. Bulgaria
   b. Austria
   c. Albania
   d. Germany

7. Which Caribbean island was named after a day of the week?

   a. Jamaica
   b. Grenada
   c. Cuba
   d. Dominica

8. Which country's name means "resplendent land" in Sanskrit?

   a. India
   b. Sri Lanka
   c. Myanmar
   d. Iran

9. Which island's name means "terraced bay" in Mandarin?

   a. Taiwan
   b. Hainan
   c. Honshu
   d. Hokkaido

10. Zimbabwe is a Shona word meaning what?

    a. Land of kings
    b. River people
    c. Settled country
    d. House of stone

BRAINSNACK® Impossible Path

Which color (1–3) should replace the letter A?

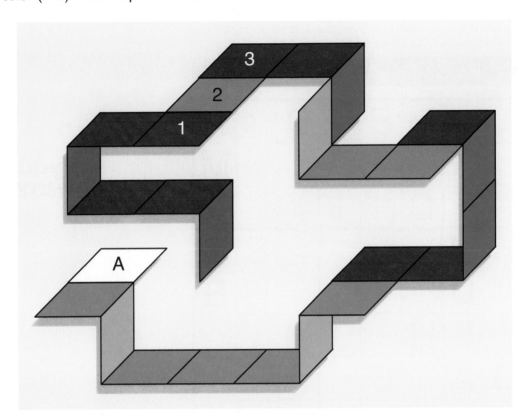

LETTER LINE

Put a letter in each of the squares below to make a word that describes something conventional. The number clues refer to other words that can be made from the whole.

1 2 7 3 4 9 6 8 FLAVOR MEAT • 2 7 1 9 10 8 4 6 MILITARY EQUIPMENT
1 3 5 8 7 PERSON WHO HOARDS MONEY; • 5 6 2 1 10 8 7 TO SPEAK FALTERINGLY
5 3 1 10 8 7 TO COOK GENTLY

1	2	3	4	5	6	7	8	9	10

Word Sudoku

Complete the grid so that each row, each column, and each 3 x 3 frame contains the nine letters from the black box below. The hidden nine-letter word is in the diagonal from top left to bottom right.

A B C D E H I M R

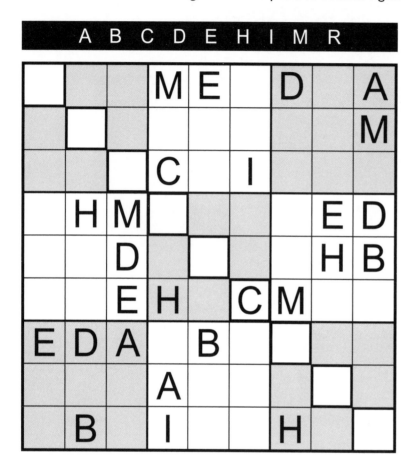

THREE-IN-ONE

Using all of the letters listed below only once, can you find the names of three mythical creatures?

A C C E E H H I I I M N N N O O P R R U X

TRIVIA QUIZ A Tribal Gathering

From the four possibilities provided, pick the correct answer about world tribes.

1. In which country do the Yanomami people mostly live?
   a. Scotland
   b. Luxembourg
   c. Denmark
   d. Brazil

2. What country do the majority of Maoris call home?
   a. Canada
   b. South Africa
   c. New Zealand
   d. China

3. On which continent do the pygmy people live?
   a. Africa
   b. Asia
   c. South America
   d. Australia

4 Which of these groups campaigns for tribal peoples' rights?
   a. Amnesty International
   b. Survival
   c. Médicins Sans Frontières
   d. Friends of the Earth

5. Which river delta is the homeland of the Ogoni people?
   a. Mekong Delta
   b. Denube Delta
   c. Niger Delta
   d. Mississippi Delta

6. The Ogiek live in the Mau Forest of which country?
   a. Kenya
   b. Libya
   c. Yemen
   d. Iran

7. Which desert is home to the Tuareg?
   a. Gobi Desert
   b. Namib Desert
   c. Sahara Desert
   d. Atacama Desert

8. In which part of Africa do most Hutus and Tutsis live?
   a. Horn of Africa
   b. Central Africa
   c. Western Africa
   d. Madagascar

9. The Himba live in Namibia and which other country?
   a. Angola
   b. Somalia
   c. Mauritania
   d. Gabon

10. Which country is home to the Mursi, Bodi, and Konso tribes?
   a. Morocco
   b. Ethiopia
   c. Argentina
   d. Vietnam

Weights

With the exception of puzzle 1, the same rules apply for each of the weights and scales below. The object is to make each set of scales balance by placing all the supplied weights in the pans – one weight per pan. The weight of the rods and pans can be ignored, and the stripes on each rod are of exactly the same length.

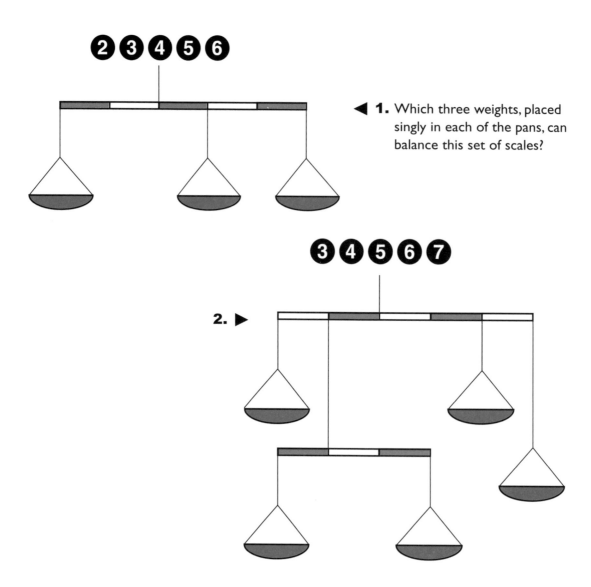

2 3 4 5 6

◀ **1.** Which three weights, placed singly in each of the pans, can balance this set of scales?

3 4 5 6 7

2. ▶

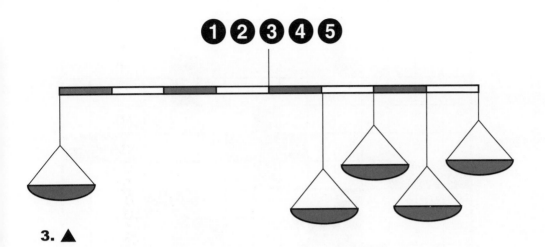

3. ▲

4. ▶

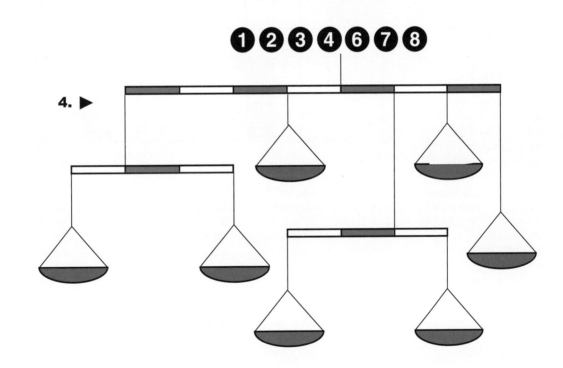

Themeless 4

ACROSS

1 Pheasant nest
5 What a candidate projects
10 Hambletonian gait
14 Hibernia
15 Nine-ball shot
16 Decor change
17 It has its highs and lows
19 "If I Were ___": Beyoncé
20 Groups of nine
21 *The Boys of Summer* team
23 Memorized, old-style
24 Billiard cushion
25 Conceit
27 Round figures
30 After a while
33 Doberman in *Up*
35 *Die Fledermaus* role
36 *Star Trek: Voyager* menace
37 Seaport of New Guinea
38 Rapper Snoop ___
39 Sweet roll
40 Lower-back bones
42 "Orinoco Flow" singer
43 Complete disorder
46 Beliefs, for short
48 Phoenix neighbor
49 Recon squad
53 Amelia Earhart's plane
56 Outdoor dining spot
57 Anderson in *Stroker Ace*
58 Italian ham
60 Quilt stuffing
61 Splash
62 *Judge Dredd* actress Joan
63 Feud leader "Devil ___" Hatfield
64 Niagara Falls sounds
65 Chapeau holder

DOWN

1 Stair post
2 Sherlock's love
3 Rigg in *The Hospital*
4 Diarist's activity
5 Lemonade alternative
6 Planet visited by Flash Gordon
7 Kind of wrestling
8 Push
9 Trading places
10 Like a Sophocles play
11 Insurgency
12 Methane doesn't have one
13 Fisher-Price products
18 Cradle rocker
22 ___ es Salaam
26 Set at ease
27 Oteri in *The Ant Bully*
28 Sharply defined
29 *The Forsyte ___*: Galsworthy
30 "Dancing Queen" group
31 Part of speech
32 Tannenbaum danglers
34 Lobbyists' org.
38 Destroy
40 More brainy
41 Views
44 Say aloud
45 Dallas hrs.
47 Husband of Paris
50 Blooming early
51 Square-dance group
52 Sierra ___
53 Napoleon's isle of exile
54 Make advances
55 With the bow, to violinists
56 Industrial giant
59 Rock-___ (jukebox brand)

WORD POWER Personality

Whatever your personality type, you'll win friends and influence people with a good vocabulary. See which of these words related to character you can define—and perhaps which defines you.

. . . .

1. **craven** ('kray-ven) *adj.*—
A: reckless. B: fussy. C: cowardly.

2. **picaresque** (pi-kuh-'resk) *adj.*—A: like a daring rascal.
B: good-looking on camera.
C: standoffish.

3. **recluse** ('reh-kloos) *n.*—
A: group leader. B: hermit.
C: problem solver.

4. **narcissist** ('nar-suh-sist) *n.*—
A: generous giver.
B: self-absorbed sort.
C: analytical type.

5. **ingratiate** (in-'gray-shee-ayt) *v.*—
A: eat impulsively.
B: attempt to control.
C: try to gain favor.

6. **acolyte** ('a-kuh-liyt) *n.*—
A: follower. B: braggart.
C: daredevil.

7. **bon vivant** (bon-vee-'vahnt) *n.*—
A: good listener.
B: trusted ally.
C: lover of fine dining.

8. **sanguine** ('san-gwin) *adj.*—
A: optimistic. B: melancholy.
C: shy.

9. **choleric** ('kah-luh-rik) *adj.*—
A: logical.
B: health-conscious.
C: hot-tempered.

10. **congenial** (kuhn-'gee-nee-uhl) *adj.*—A: unreliable.
B: given to gossip.
C: friendly.

11. **bloviate** ('blo-vee-ayt) *v.*—
A: get angry.
B: rant pompously.
C: commit petty crimes.

12. **venal** ('vee-nal) *adj.*—
A: virtuous. B: corruptible.
C: interfering.

13. **bumptious** ('bump-shus) *adj.*—
A: pushy.
B: countrified.
C: roly-poly.

14. **altruistic** ('al-troo-is-tik) *adj.*—
A: honest.
B: kind to others.
C: quick to change.

15. **bohemian** (bo-'hee-mee-in) *adj.*—A: macho guy.
B: nonconformist.
C: picker of arguments.

Sudoku

Fill in the grid so that each row, each column, and each 3 x 3 frame contains every number from 1 to 9.

				7				
								1
		4		5		3		
7				8	6			9
3			1	9			2	
					4		6	7
5	3	2	9	1	8			
	7	1	6				8	
8						2		3

triVia

• Which film contains the song "Moon River"?

SYMBOL SUMS

Can you work out these number sums using three of these four symbols? ✚ ─ ÷ ✕

11 ☐ 3 ☐ 13 ☐ 5 = 4

Word Ladders

Convert the word at the top of the ladders into the word at the bottom, using all the rungs in between. On each rung, you must put a valid word that has the same letters as the word above it, apart from one letter change. There may be more than one way to achieve this.

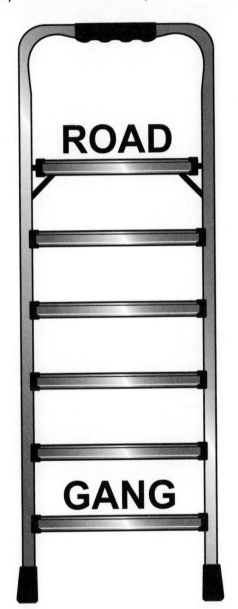

ROAD

GANG

BANK

NOTE

Futoshiki

Fill in the 5 x 5 grid with the numbers from 1 to 5 once per row and column, while following the greater-than/lesser-than symbols shown. There is only one valid solution that can be reached through logic and clear thinking alone!

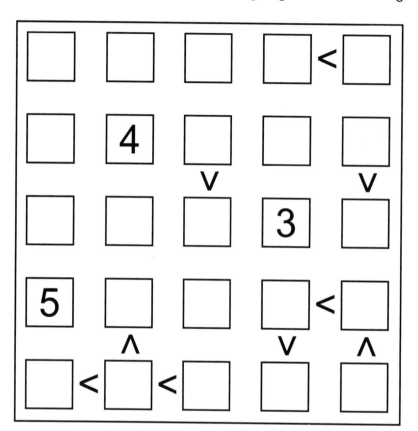

do you KNOW

Which plant family do apples belong to?

TRIANAGRAM

Three-word groups of anagrams are also called triplets or trianagrams.
Complete the group:

C I T R U S   _ _ _ _ _ _   _ _ _ _ _ _

CROSSWORD **Not Related**

ACROSS

1 Sinks down
5 Tour-de-France end
10 Nutmeg spice
14 Requiring first aid
15 *Gone With the Wind* hero
16 "There oughta be ___!"
17 Indonesian islands
18 Willow twig
19 Glazed fabric
20 Flora, Fauna, and Merryweather
23 Sawbuck
24 Sharp
25 F-16 letters
27 Navigation tool
30 Pour
33 ___ nest (hoax)
35 Case for pins
36 In toto
37 Asphalt
38 The Liberty Tree, for one
39 Willing, in verse
41 Old Testament prophet
43 *Spamalot* creator Eric
44 Hill of Washington
46 Tide influence
48 Parliamentary shout
49 Announce a verdict
53 Exempt from new statute regulations
58 ___-Dixie Stores
59 Close to amber
60 Dying star
61 Suffix for usher
62 Memorize, e.g.
63 One-armed bandit
64 *The Water Horse* loch
65 ___ Kross puzzle
66 City near Padua

DOWN

1 Beam of light
2 Mystiques
3 Erosion sea wall
4 Breastbone
5 Write computer code
6 "I see!"
7 Tara in *American Reunion*
8 Gossiped-about couple
9 Scorecard numbers
10 Jungle knife
11 Estranged
12 *The Alienist* author
13 Mouflon mamas
21 "Definitely!"
22 Cowboy Ritter
26 Causing death
27 Blood part
28 Void companion
29 Chronology
30 Mohs' number 1
31 Charles Lamb
32 Celesteville citizens
34 Rally yell
40 Ralph who plays Voldemort
41 Chesapeake Bay city
42 Neoterics
43 Aromatherapy need
45 A Lincoln
47 Opposite of 'neath
50 Emulated ones
51 Fairway clump
52 Mother's kin
53 Verdon in *Cocoon*
54 ___ of passage
55 Taiwan computer company
56 Cuisine choice
57 Towel designation

TRIVIAL PURSUIT Long Road Home

A bestseller in 1939 and a Pulitzer Prize winner, *The Grapes of Wrath* by John Steinbeck was also controversial. The saga about Dust Bowl migrants was banned in several places, including Kern County, California, where the story's fictional family ends up. The controversy didn't stop Hollywood from making the story into a movie in 1940.

WHAT DO YOU REMEMBER ABOUT THIS CLASSIC?

1 The title comes from what Civil War tune?

_____

2 What is the family's last name, which sounds like the Bible's Job?

_____

3 Some scenes were shot in these three states—part of the route real Dust Bowl migrants took to California.

_____

4 Which actor, speaking as Tom, declares, "Wherever there's a fight so hungry people can eat, I'll be there"?

_____

5 Which actress won the Academy Award in a supporting role for her portrayal of Ma?

_____

6 Though he was better known for his historical Westerns, the director took home the Oscar for this movie about a more contemporary West.

_____

7 What did John Ford ban from the set on the grounds that it was not in keeping with the tone of the picture?

_____

8 The family is forced to leave their home in Oklahoma to do what/ where?

_____

9 What does Uncle John give to the children?

_____

BRAINSNACK® Building Blocks

Imagine you have the task of recreating the construction shown below. You have seen it only from the angle shown in the illustration and need to recreate that view. How many blocks will you need?

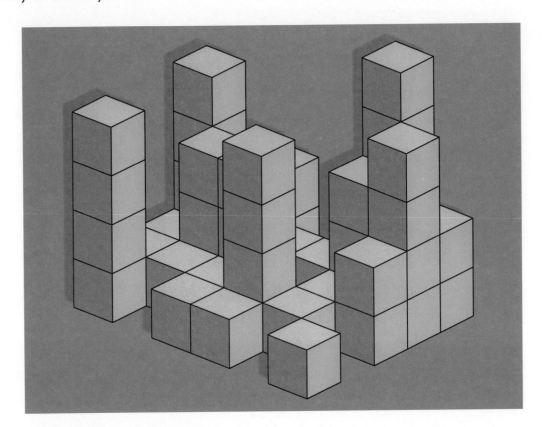

DOODLE PUZZLE

A doodle puzzle is a combination of images, letters, and/or numbers that represent a word or a concept. If you cannot solve a doodle puzzle, do not look at the answer right away. Think hard—and outside the box.

Picasso

All the words are hidden vertically, horizontally, or diagonally—in both directions. The letters that remain unused form a sentence from left to right.

```
P I A E E S U R R E A L I S M
E L N S H D S F I T O M N R H
R O O O T R D T I S Y O O A K
I L L R N A E U I T H T M N P
O A E A I I P B L L P O I O A
D P C I S N R C A L L R S S C
S O R P B A E A U A D L I N I
J T A E A P S C P D U P I T N
O A B T O S S E R U G I F R
E H C R A I E L L E C R A M E
R T R Q A T D M O U G I N S U
V U C E U W I U M A D R I D G
U E I H M E L H T N O L G A C
E A N Z I U L I C S U V A R S
O V E S A N S I V N D D A T E
C H A N G E G E N I O Y E I U
A M O R O U S S U E C C I S L
N P A C U B I S M M R I S T B
```

- ABSINTHE
- AMOROUS
- ARTIST
- BARCELONA
- BLUE
- CHANGE
- CIVIL WAR
- CONCHITA
- CUBISM
- DEPRESSED
- DRINK
- ETCHINGS
- EVA
- FIGURES
- GUERNICA
- JACQUELINE
- LOLA
- MADRID
- MARCELLE
- MOTIFS
- MOUGINS
- MUSEUM
- NUDES
- OEUVRE
- OLGA
- PALOMA
- PERIODS
- ROSE
- RUIZ
- SCULPTOR
- SPANIARD
- STILL LIFE
- STUDIO
- SURREALISM

CROSSWORD # Three Amigos

ACROSS

1 Estonian, e.g.
5 Not true, in a way
10 Easily split mineral
14 "Say ___ if you mean ..."
15 Tennis star Petrova
16 Shrinking Asian sea
17 Three "amigos"
20 Components
21 Home of the Maple Leafs
22 Sign outside a hit musical
23 Kind of wheel
24 Goddess of the hunt
28 *Mano-a-mano* man
32 Main off Maine
33 *A Bell for ___*: Hersey
35 Become used to
36 Twenty machines
38 Utterly exhausted
40 Kitten's plaything
41 Jones of the Stones
43 Rocky Mountain state
45 Insect egg
46 Kind of greens
48 Sadden
50 180 degrees from WSW
51 Hiroshima river
52 "Very impressive"
56 River in an Enya song
60 Three "amigos"
62 Ceramic plate
63 Side drum
64 Tipperary locale
65 Pair of oxen
66 Lee and Teasdale
67 Crème ___ crème

DOWN

1 *Back to the Future* bully
2 Gillette razor
3 Of the congregation
4 Flybelt fly
5 *Blade Runner* characters
6 Sad bugle call
7 G&S princess
8 Buoyant air
9 Puget Sound port
10 Piano wood
11 Club for Ernie Els
12 Links rental
13 Art Pepper's sax
18 Designer Kamali
19 Speak to the masses
24 "Easy ___!"
25 Backward-looking
26 Sri Lankan language
27 Tasty
28 Single-celled organism
29 Bounty hunter "Dog" Chapman
30 Rootstock used in perfumes
31 Checks for letters?
34 Homer Simpson's neighbor
37 Pitchers, of a kind
39 Conjectures
42 Small iPods
44 Sight-related
47 Inattentive
49 Seeded
52 Treads the boards
53 Riding crop
54 *Rooster Cogburn* heroine
55 Tracy's *Hairspray* mom
56 Gumbo veggie
57 Off-Broadway award
58 Permanent result
59 Performance halls
61 Musical talent

Spot the Differences

Find the nine differences in the image on the bottom right.

Which U.S. state is
Mount St. Helens
located in?

_____

trivia

- Who was known as the
  "King of Swing"?

_____

Word Wheel

How many words of three or more letters, each including the letter at the center of the wheel, can you make from this diagram? No plurals or conjugations. We've found 16, including one nine-letter word. Can you do better?

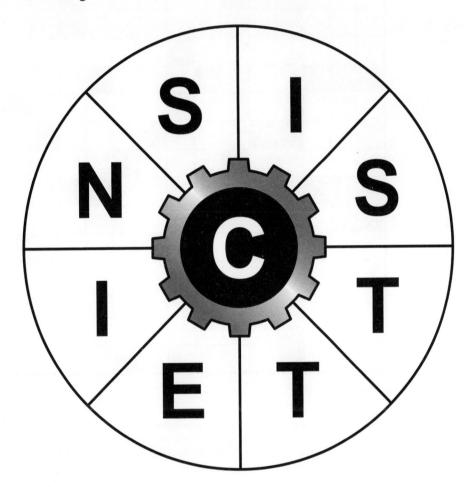

What three-letter word belongs between the word at left and the word at right, so that the first and second word, and the second and third word, each form a common compound word or phrase?

K N E E _ _ _ S I Z E

That's Life

ACROSS

1 Let up
6 Horrify
11 Soccer official
14 Brought back
15 Greta in "Camille"
16 Popular detergent
17 Start of a quote by Mary Roberts Rinehart
19 Actress Joanne
20 Needlepoint designs?
21 Ammunition wagon
23 Browser bookmark
24 Humpback herd
25 Jellied fish
26 More of quote
31 Not either
32 Palindromic cheer
33 Group that works with the FBI
34 Pear-shaped fruit
37 "His Master's Voice" company
39 Calvin of fashion
43 Harvest goddess
45 Spasmodic sound
47 Auguste Dupin's creator
48 More of quote
52 Doctorate prequel
54 Assistance
55 Canister
56 W Indonesian island
58 Cuba in *Red Tails*
62 Hedged investor, for short
63 End of quote
65 Wander aimlessly
66 One in a brown study
67 Gnawed away
68 New Hampshire river
69 Splurge
70 Sour

DOWN

1 Smell ___ (suspect)
2 Fleck of jazz
3 Mine access
4 "Tsk tsk"
5 Take by intimidation
6 *Rock of* ___ (2012)
7 Handle roughly
8 Rock's ___ Harum
9 Roughed up
10 Evil Aesir member
11 Sudan neighbor
12 Documentarian Morris
13 Stravinsky's sprites
18 Sucker

22 Floral leaf
24 Amped
26 Film director Lee
27 Merloni or Piniella
28 Iwo Jima flag raiser Hayes
29 One end of a grin?
30 "Horrors!"
35 Magician's interjection
36 Suitable
38 Have it bad
40 Pollution control gp.
41 Charged atom
42 Kelly or Rorem
44 New company

46 Programming language
48 Letter before mu
49 Be a go-between
50 Reddish-blue
51 *Bewitched* mother witch
52 Mulberry family member
53 Like Mayberry
57 Robbins and Rice
58 River of S France
59 Novello of *The Lodger*
60 Place for a chat
61 *Rogue River Feud* author
64 1/100 yen

BRAINSNACK® **Towering**

A red tower is visible through an airplane window. With which tower (1–11) on the floor plan does this red tower correspond?

WORD WALL

Beginning at the left side of the wall, make a word by adding one group of letters from each column as you move left to right. When you have found the first word, go back to the second column and start the next word, gathering one group of letters from each column and so on until all the letters are used to make six words.

THE | RMO | DER | CTR | ALI | ANT
     | SEN | SAT | ITI | RAS | TER
     | | ELE | ION | OME | SEA
     | | MAB | NAU | ION | ICE
     | | | | NER | STS

The Puzzled Librarian

The new library assistant accidentally bumped into the Good Reads Notice Board, and the magnetic letters all fell off. The librarian remembered the authors' names but needs some help to get the titles right, as the chief librarian will be back in ten minutes!

GOOD READS NOTICE BOARD

1 BLITHELY DROWSE by Kevin Powers
2 SHIELDED MITTENS by Jami Attenberg
3 HOOT TWEETS by Ian McEwan
4 BREATHE WHOOP FIT by Charles Duhigg
5 SHOCKED FRONTIER by Bee Wilson
6 ECHO VET by Ron Rash
7 A GRATEFUL APE by Philip Kerr
8 NAVIGABLE SLOTH by Tanis Rideout
9 A FIELDER by Alice Munro
10 EWE IN KNITWEAR by Maeve Binchy

SANDWICH

What four-letter word belongs between the word at left and the word at right, so that the first and second word, and the second and third word, each form a common compound word or phrase?

B O A R D _ _ _ _ W A Y

CROSSWORD 2012 Hits

ACROSS

1 Starbuck's captain
5 Wig base
10 Mama llamas
14 Brainsick
15 Seasonal song
16 Seedy joint
17 2012 Luke Bryan hit
19 Brainstorm
20 Getty in *The Golden Girls*
21 Object to
23 Essential
24 Puccini song
25 Golf course designer Jones
27 Nudged
30 Dorothy's ___ slippers
33 Miles of jazz
35 Alliance formed in 1949
36 Prefix for bar
37 Binge
38 Heyerdahl's ___-Tiki
39 Coughs up
41 They're taken on the stand
43 Budget item
44 Ben in *The Company Men*
46 English metro
48 Let off steam
49 Cloud in Orion
53 Purplish-red
56 Picked up the tab
57 "I say ...."
58 2012 Pitbull hit
60 Russo of *One Good Cop*
61 Cultural mores
62 Jewish month after Ab
63 Alan in "Shane"
64 Witherspoon in *Legally Blonde*
65 Parched

DOWN

1 John on the *Mayflower*
2 Cowboy's companion
3 Deep-felt
4 Drought-stricken
5 Read the riot act to
6 Stocking candy
7 Suffix for honor
8 Stunt pilot's stunt
9 Singular opposites
10 Printing
11 2012 Katy Perry hit
12 Holiday times
13 Pants part
18 "Zitronen" painter Paul
22 Globe
26 *Wheel of Fortune* host
27 Furlongs in a mile
28 Lord Wimsey's alma mater
29 "___ Worry, Be Happy"
30 Kelly of talk TV
31 F-16 letters
32 2012 Justin Bieber hit
34 Brewery tank
40 Shut forcefully
41 Columbus Day month
42 First light
43 Buying incentives
45 Dash sizes
47 "___ there, done that!"
50 Employable
51 Big-eyed primate
52 "Chasing Pavements" singer
53 *Up* protagonist
54 Ostrich look-alike
55 Mendel of the Foo Fighters
56 Some boxing wins
59 Mandy's *Evita* role

Symbolic Science

Every element on the periodic table is abbreviated to make scientific notations easier to follow. Can you name the correct element based on its symbol?

1. Ar
  a. Argon
  b. Arsenic
  c. Americium

2. Br
  a. Bohrium
  b. Boron
  c. Bromine

3. Ca
  a. Carbon
  b. Californium
  c. Calcium

4. Co
  a. Copper
  b. Cobalt
  c. Chlorine

5. S
  a. Sulphur
  b. Sodium
  c. Selenium

6. Ag
  a. Gold
  b. Silver
  c. Argon

7. Pt
  a. Platinum
  b. Plutonium
  c. Potassium

8. Ni
  a. Nitrogen
  b. Niobium
  c. Nickel

9. Rh
  a. Rhodium
  b. Rhenium
  c. Ruthenium

10. Pb
  a. Polonium
  b. Lead
  c. Phosphorus

trivia

- What gas is responsible for making birthday balloons a delightful part of any party?

_____

Hourglass

Starting in the middle, each word in the top half has the letters of the word below it, plus a new letter, and each word in the bottom half has the letters of the word above it, plus a new letter.

(1) Anticipate

(2) Approval

(3) Bored

(4) Prepare for publiction

(5) Day

(6) Business deal

(7) Ribbon

(8) Humidify

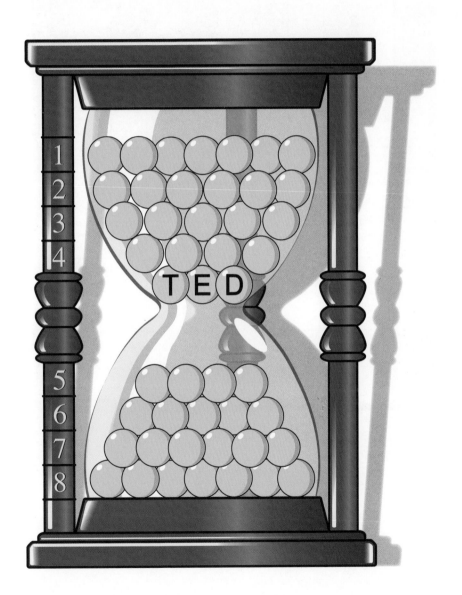

Maze

Enter the maze, pass over all tanks from behind, and then exit.
You may not pass through a grid space more than once, and may not
enter a grid space in the line of a tank you have not yet passed over.

How many players
are on a
field hockey team?

THREE-IN-ONE

Using all of the letters listed below only once, can you find the names of three deserts?

A A A A A A B C C G H H H I I M N O T U U

CROSSWORD Non-Violence

ACROSS

1 American League 2005 MVP
5 Bizet work
10 Behave
13 Hindu royal
14 ___ clef
16 Caprine comment
17 Start of a Roger Moore quote
20 French farewell
21 Follower's suffix
22 Med nurse's concerns
23 Spanish ladies, for short
25 City in Spain or Ohio
26 More of quote
31 Lake craft
32 Neither here ___ there
33 In the thick of
37 Borneo macaque
38 Chemist Lavoisier
41 Del Potro serve
42 Nomadic Finn
44 "Somebody Stole My ___"
45 Baking potatoes
47 More of quote
50 Band-Aid spot
53 Guitarist Atkins
54 Put in a row
55 Class for U.S. immigrants
57 To Catch a Thief thief
61 End of quote
64 2012 Miley Cyrus film
65 Mexican wrap
66 Uncluttered
67 U-turn from WSW
68 Superman's family
69 Part of B.A.

DOWN

1 Madama Butterfly solo
2 McNally partner
3 R.E.M.'s "The ___ Love"
4 Strips of power
5 Bruin Hall-of-Famer
6 Refinement
7 Shoot out
8 Autumn tool
9 French donkey
10 Ill-treat
11 Wove rattan
12 "The Eighth Muse"
15 Extra charge
18 Cry of discovery
19 Israel's Meir
24 All excited
25 Silver problem
26 H–M bridge
27 Queen of Olympus
28 ___ on the shoulder
29 Nancy Springer detective
30 Miss Piggy's pronoun
34 Hawaiian fish, for short
35 Mouse target
36 Office piece
39 Looked like Tweety?
40 1990 Wimbledon winner
43 Alicia Keys' instrument
46 City near Horseshoe Curve
48 Copycats
49 Named, humorously
50 Stone marten
51 Designer Throckmorton
52 Winchester
55 Irregular French verb
56 Gerald Ford's cat
58 Afrikaner
59 "___ first you don't succeed ..."
60 Young newts
62 Cry of fright
63 "You rang?"

CROSSWORD ▸ Hotel Transylvania

ACROSS

1 Aftershave item
5 Deflect
10 First name in spies
14 Stone with color flashes
15 *Law & Order* actress de la Garza
16 Round cheese
17 Frankenstein in *Hotel Transylvania*
19 Tibetan VIP
20 Tabby's cry
21 Like an angry lobster?
23 Attack with abandon
26 Pacific eagles
27 Ladybugs, e.g.
29 Military unit
32 Healthy
33 Doubtful
35 Hydroxyl compound
36 Cockney residence
37 ___ Aviv
38 Carrier of genetic code
39 City near Sparks, Nevada
41 Becomes boring
43 Bed piece
44 Florida menu fish
46 Wheaties star
48 Low or drive
49 Brought up
50 Where Athens is
53 Chicken
54 *Brokeback Mountain* heroine
55 Griffin in *Hotel Transylvania*
60 Bard
61 Deliver a formal speech
62 Apt anagram of "vile"
63 Magnitude
64 Auditions
65 Animal homes

DOWN

1 "Tik ___": Ke$ha
2 Magilla or Mighty Joe Young
3 Facilities, for short
4 *An Inconvenient Truth* subject
5 Sweet-talked
6 "There oughta be ___!"
7 Dodge truck
8 Lowest Sudoku numbers
9 Total control
10 Jumble
11 Dracula in *Hotel Transylvania*
12 Submissive
13 *Diary of ___ Black Woman* (2005)
18 "Be" singer Diamond
22 ___ tu: Verdi aria
23 Rejects vehemently
24 *H.M.S. Pinafore* roles
25 Mavis in *Hotel Transylvania*
28 It's played with a plectrum
29 Stephenie Meyer heroine
30 Give
31 Floating on air
34 Disney collectible
40 Drive
41 Green gem
42 Takes steps
43 Made red-faced?
45 Opera pal of *Cav*
47 Borders
50 Dental concerns
51 *The Time Machine* race
52 It rises in the Bernese Alps
53 Alicia in *Urban Legend*
56 ___ in Victor
57 NYC's Lexington
58 Hubbub
59 2002 Open Championship winner

Sport Maze

Draw the shortest way from the ball to the goal. You can only move along vertical and horizontal lines, not along diagonal lines. The figure on each square indicates the number of squares the ball must move in the same direction. You can change direction at each stop.

3	5	5	5	5	3
3	4	3	3	3	4
5	2	3	1	3	3
2		0	3	3	1
3	4	4	1	4	4
4	5	5	5	4	3

do you KNOW?

How many tennis Grand Slams are there?

ONE LETTER LESS OR MORE

The word on the right side contains the letters of the word on the left side, plus or minus the letter in the middle. One letter is already in the right place.

ORNAMENT +G [ ][ ][ ] N [ ][ ][ ][ ]

Directions

You are in a city with streets of equal length that always cross each other perpendicularly. At every street corner, there is a traffic sign that indicates the direction of the main road. Start at sign A. After which traffic sign (B–X) will you arrive once again at intersection A?

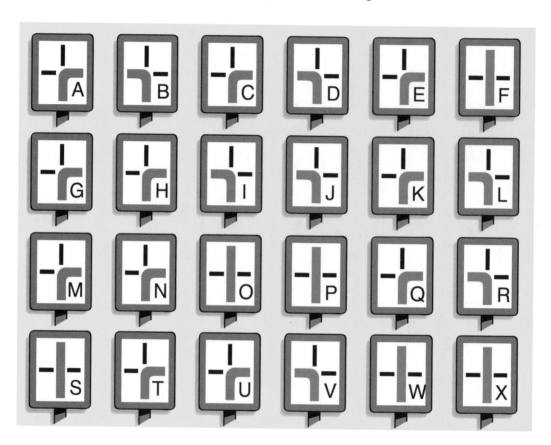

BLOCK ANAGRAM

Form the word that is described in the parentheses, using the letters above the grid. Extra letters are already in the right place.

SHORT-TERM (heavy rain or hail along with thunder and lightning)

☐ ☐ U N D ☐ ☐ ☐ ☐ ☐ ☐

WORD SEARCH **Kitchen Utensils**

All the words are hidden vertically, horizontally, or diagonally—in both directions. The letters that remain unused form a sentence from left to right.

```
E G O N L N I T G N I K A B O
D F K I I L C A S S E R O L E
T C I H K P I R E T A R G E N
U T L N K E G R E N E E S O I
C L I R K S T N G N M L P A K
O E O J W D O T I R K E I D P
F F F U I N A A L L N E C R U
F P N I T H R E E E L P E A C
E W I C K T I T R C H O C O G
E H T E S H S U R B E N R B N
F I M R T Y R E L T U C E G I
I S N O R I E L F F A W A N R
L K U C G H N M O R E P M I U
T L E L F I S H P A N R S P S
E T A L P R E R O C E L P P A
R S P A T U L A A X S A O O E
S C A L E S N T I F A S O H M
T E R A N D E M A S I E N C R
```

- APPLE CORER
- BAKING TIN
- BREAD KNIFE
- BRUSH
- CASSEROLE
- CHOPPING BOARD
- COFFEE FILTER
- CUTLERY
- FISH PAN
- FORK
- GLASS
- GRATER
- GRILL
- ICE CREAM SPOON
- JUICER
- KETTLE
- MEASURING CUP
- MIXER
- OPENER
- PEELER
- PIE TIN
- PLATE
- ROLLING PIN
- SCALES
- SPATULA
- STRAINER
- TIN FOIL
- WAFFLE IRON
- WHISK

Word Sudoku

Complete the grid so that each row, each column, and each 3 x 3 frame contains the nine letters from the black box below. The hidden nine-letter word is in the diagonal from top left to bottom right.

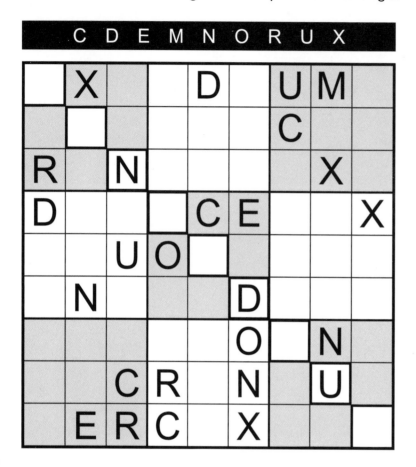

C D E M N O R U X

	X			D		U	M	
						C		
R		N					X	
D				C	E			X
		U	O					
	N				D			
					O		N	
		C	R		N		U	
	E	R	C		X			

do you KNOW?

Petra is located in which country?

Futoshiki

Fill in the 5 x 5 grid with the numbers from 1 to 5 once per row and column, while following the greater-than/lesser-than symbols shown. There is only one valid solution that can be reached through logic and clear thinking alone!

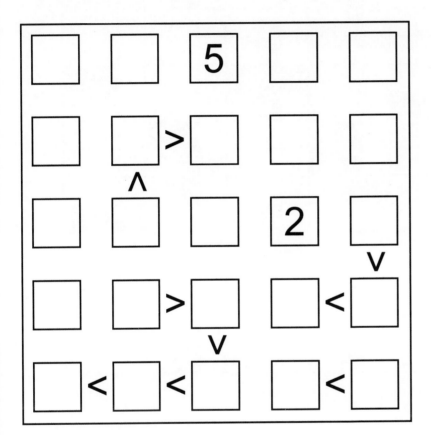

trivia

- Who starred as Clarice Starling in a 1991 film?

TRIANAGRAM

Three-word groups of anagrams are also called triplets or trianagrams.
Complete the group:

TRACER _ _ _ _ _ _   _ _ _ _ _ _

Themeless 5

ACROSS

1 Ocular layer
5 Joe of the Eagles
10 Thank the singer
14 Garnet and ruby
15 Pointed
16 Kerry locale
17 Locale of the 2010 Olympics
20 Bening in *The Women*
21 Takes to a higher court
22 More accessible
23 Helvetica, e.g.
24 Singles
26 "___ High and Low": A-ha
29 Broadway opener
32 On the up and up
34 "Texas tea"
35 Three-___ sloth
36 Cross-shaped letter
37 Choreographer White
38 First to homer 500 times in N.L.
39 Link to the Internet
41 Like garage-sale items
42 Silky-haired feline
45 Pipsqueak
47 God of love
48 Firefighter's job
52 Cherubic
55 Removed
56 *The Blue Angel* star
58 Viva voce
59 Enlist
60 *Lost ___ Mancha* (2002)
61 Dixie veggies
62 Overwhelms
63 Ball-___ hammer

DOWN

1 Citified
2 Phileas Fogg's creator
3 Saffron's *Ab Fab* mother
4 Space rock
5 Profligate
6 Pain in the neck
7 Violinist Jean-___ Ponty
8 Greek promenade
9 Like a good scout
10 Fix firmly
11 Drinks
12 Nutmeg feature
13 Veggies that roll
18 New Orleans-to-Houston route
19 Informed about
25 American saint
26 Vitriolic one
27 Inches in a span
28 Delighted
29 Surmounting
30 ___ d'Azur
31 Four-letter word
33 The Omnipotent
37 Surpass
39 Camp Pendleton group
40 ___ *Wedding* (1995)
43 Olfactory input
44 Captive of Hercules
46 Nutcracker suite
49 *Dirty Rotten Scoundrels* star
50 Word of surrender
51 Hawke in *Great Expectations*
52 Island off China
53 Honshu hub
54 Lincoln's coin
55 "Unison" singer Celine
57 Soul group ___ Hill

Horoscope

Fill in the grid so that every row, every column and every frame of six boxes contains six different symbols: health, work, money, happiness, family, and love. Look at the row or column that corresponds with your sign of the zodiac and find out which of the six symbols are important for you today. The symbols appear in increasing order of importance (1–6). It's up to you to translate the meaning of each symbol to your specific situation.

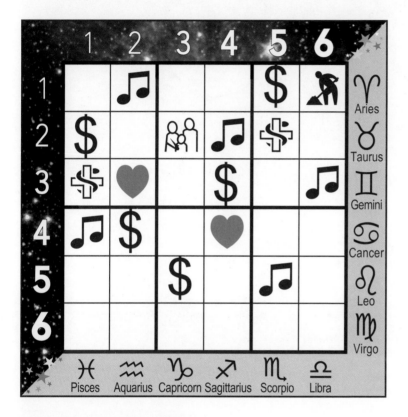

delete ONE

Delete one letter from

I'M A DREAM

and find something mythical.

LETTERBLOCKS

Move the letterblocks around so that words associated with birds are formed on the top and bottom rows. In some blocks the letter from the top row has been switched with the letter from the bottom row.

Deuce

Which letter should replace the question mark?

FRIENDS

What do the following words have in common?

LEAF GAUNT TRIP BRACE SCAR BOOK

CROSSWORD # Love at the Movies

ACROSS

1 John Wayne and Maureen O'Hara star in this romance set in Ireland, 3 words
7 He was asked to "play it" in *Casablanca*
9 First lady
10 Miss. neighbor
12 Star of *The Philadelphia Story*
13 See 30 across
16 Compete with a rival
17 Cry deeply
18 Murphy's _____
19 Tomato type
22 Katharine Hepburn played one in *The Philadelphia Story*
25 Small ensemble
29 Ollie's partner in comedy
30 1957 tear-jerker, with 31 across, 32 across and 13 across
31 See 30 across
32 See 30 across
33 Rare baseball game, 2 words
38 Rainbow curve
40 *Gone With The Wind* plantation house
41 *Exodus* author
44 _____ Rogers, comics hero
46 Historic time
47 Starred with Joel of 34 down, Claudette _____
48 *To _____, With Love*
50 Temperature control, for short
51 Hawaiian coffee
52 See 21 down
53 Bismarck's state

DOWN

1 Romantic drama with Humphrey Bogart and Katharine Hepburn on a rickety boat, 3 words
2 "... happily _____ after"
3 Savory taste
4 Test
5 1956 Charlton Heston role
6 Egg drink
7 Rhett's belle
8 1960s music style out of Detroit, MI
11 Marvin of *The Dirty Dozen*
14 "The Loco-Motion" singer Little _____
15 Audrey Hepburn won an Oscar for her role in this romantic comedy _____ *Holiday*
20 *Ben-Hur* studio
21 Romantic comedy starring Spencer Tracy and Katharine Hepburn, with 52 across, 4 words
23 Prefix with metric
24 Musical ability
26 Lennon's widow
27 Teases
28 A lot (poetic)
34 Joel _____, star of the romantic comedy *The Palm Beach Story*
35 Holmes' sidekick
36 He directed the romantic comedy *It Happened One Night*
37 Moonshine
38 First word in a Beatles album
39 Regret
42 Luxury car emblem on the hood
43 One of Shakespeare's bad guys
45 Unit of gold measurement, abbr.
47 Dog's nemesis
49 Neither Rep. nor Dem.

CROSSWORD   Geek Squad

ACROSS

1 Plain vanilla
5 Short of
11 Barrel
14 Fanning in *We Bought a Zoo*
15 Italian cheese
16 Notable time
17 PC screen at Carnegie?
19 ___ Kippur
20 Tentacled fish
21 Bud of Eminem
23 Opus for nine
24 Celsius freezing point
25 Flip a coin
28 Winged
31 Cross word
34 Rhodes of talk radio
36 Alpine region
37 "Holy Toledo!"
39 Satellites
41 Dame Everage
42 Pulsate painfully
44 Kind of bread
46 Sloth, for one
47 Sorrow
49 Belarussian, e.g.
51 Mussolini moniker
52 Arapaho abode
56 Egg containers
59 Taking no sides
61 Gold of *Entourage*
62 PC accessory at Disney Studios?
64 PBS series
65 *The Graduate* heroine
66 First home
67 Shelley poem
68 Hearing and smell
69 Ward in *CSI: NY*

DOWN

1 *Borstal Boy* author
2 Southwest plain
3 Microsoft cofounder Paul
4 Batter's wear
5 Middle name for Elvis
6 Danielle Steel's ___ *Eagle*
7 Roman *Space Odyssey* year
8 Imprecation
9 Forty winks
10 Harry
11 Essential surfing equipment?
12 Suffix for switch
13 Like bear meat
18 Outboard
22 *My Three Sons* son
26 Film director Mendes
27 *The ___ of Kilimanjaro*
28 Maine trees
29 Rafa Nadal's uncle/coach
30 Dash
31 Plays the ponies
32 Muslim official
33 Tough commute?
35 Homer Simpson's cry
38 Cruller
40 Tessio in *The Godfather*
43 Morphs into
45 Jazz pianist Art
48 More than forgetful
50 Nixes a bill
53 Hardly a libertine
54 Canvas holder
55 *The Vampire Diaries* heroine
56 Guitar bar
57 Teammate of Jeter
58 Flip through
59 Aloha State bird
60 Spud buds
63 ___ *for Killer*: Grafton

Sudoku

Fill in the grid so that each row, each column, and each 3 x 3 frame contains every number from 1 to 9.

				9		4		8
	3	4		1		9		
	5				8			
5							4	6
		8	3		2	7		
6	1							9
			9				7	
		2		7		8	6	
3		6		4				

do you KNOW?

Which constellation is Betelgeuse in?

_____

LETTERBLOCKS

Move the letterblocks around so that words associated with festivity are formed on the top and bottom rows. In some blocks the letter from the top row has been switched with the letter from the bottom row.

I	R	T	T	L	G	E
R	S	T	I	A	P	E

Number Cluster

Cubes showing numbers have been placed on the grid below, with some spaces left empty. Can you complete the grid by creating runs of the same number and of the same length as the number? So, where a cube with number 5 has been included on the grid, you need to create a run of five number 5's, including the cube already shown. The run can be horizontal, vertical, or both horizontal and vertical.

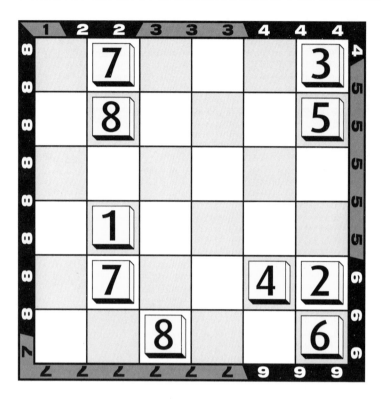

delete ONE

Delete one letter from
UNREGULATED POSER
and rearrange the rest and find somewhere to wait.

DOODLE PUZZLE

A doodle puzzle is a combination of images, letters, and/or numbers that represent a word or a concept. If you cannot solve a doodle puzzle, do not look at the answer right away. Think hard—and outside the box.

CROSSWORD # Opposite Number

ACROSS

1 Droplet
5 Bathsheba's husband
10 Bloke
14 "___ Want to Do": Sugarland
15 Sabrina's witchy aunt
16 Fourth base
17 ADA version of a Shirley Temple song?
20 Instant-replay option
21 Traveling bag
22 Mallard genus
25 Smooth, in a way
26 Barbara Stanwyck film (with *The*)
29 Vehicle for Messala
33 UN labor org.
34 Exodus memorial
36 Cycling trick
37 Facility for moms working the third shift?
41 Audition tape
42 "Hey, Soul Sister" band
43 "Horsefeathers!"
44 *Penguin Island* author France
47 Leaves stranded
49 Pedicure focus
50 On the horizon
51 Fainting spells
54 Totally legal
58 They'll never get off the ground?
63 Like the Nefud
64 *Ernani* is one
65 Simba's love
66 Contradict
67 *Finding Nemo* pelican
68 Gold or bronze award

DOWN

1 *Chicken Run* chicken
2 Mideast airline
3 Singer Nova
4 Consternation
5 Assault weapon
6 Salesman
7 Off one's feed
8 Activity
9 Sesame-honey candy
10 Some minors
11 Snake dance tribe
12 Book following Joel
13 Skunk of cartoons
18 "No fooling!"
19 Wood in *Diamonds Are Forever*
23 "___ plaisir!"
24 Makes drowsy
25 Roller-coaster sounds
26 Model Evangelista
27 Not of this world
28 Established belief
30 Musical lead-in
31 "___ Melancholy": Keats
32 First-year law school class
35 Make a blooper
38 Winter drink spiced with cloves
39 Ferrara farewell
40 Join up
45 Chaplin in *Quantum of Solace*
46 Wound
48 Kitchen bulbs
51 Pompano relative
52 Modeled
53 Lena in *Hollywood Homicide*
55 London Fog, e.g.
56 On Ventura Blvd., say
57 Pre-Soviet ruler
59 Campus in Troy, NY
60 "I ___ your pardon"
61 Have being
62 Data's android daughter

Number Targets

These puzzles are all about missing numbers. Your task is simple, but not always easy: Study the numerical patterns and sequences, and fill in the absent figure. You will find that X often marks the spot.

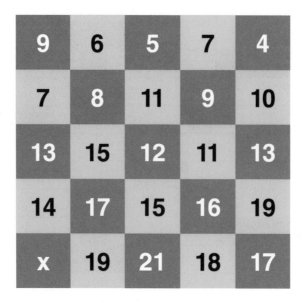

9	6	5	7	4
7	8	11	9	10
13	15	12	11	13
14	17	15	16	19
x	19	21	18	17

▲ **1.** What number should x be in this number square?

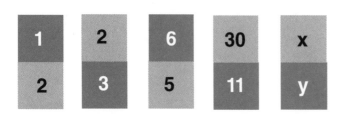

▲ **2.** What are the missing numbers x and y?

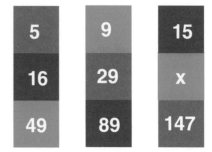

▲ **3.** What number represents x in the third column?

Amazing Number Maze

Starting at the top left-hand square, move from square to square horizontally and vertically — but not diagonally — to find your way through the maze and uncover a familiar sequence of numbers. The exit is via the top right square.

4	8	3	6
2	1	2	3
1	0	2	8
6	2	4	2

trivia

- Who designed the Guggenheim Museum in Bibao?

One Way

Try to draw this shape with one continuous line without lifting your pencil off the page and without any overlapping.

WORD WALL

Beginning at the left side of the wall, make a word by adding one group of letters from each column as you move left to right. When you have found the first word, go back to the second column and start the next word, gathering one group of letters from each column and so on until all the letters are used to make six words.

WORD SEARCH **Sound**

All the words are hidden vertically, horizontally, or diagonally—in both directions. The letters that remain unused form a sentence from left to right.

```
D O M I N A N T T O N E S O U
H E A R I N G I M P A I R E D
N D M O B L A S T R V E S I N
E C R U O S O T D E E P S N W
A V R G E N S R R T H A H O T
A S N R G E U T C U A U R I G
T O H W T M A B Y T P H I S T
G E A O U E G N A H C S L E H
E H O L P M U F F L E R L I R
S E E E S C I N O R T C E L E
U A R C L E A C O U S T I C S
A D E A I N S T R U M E N T H
L P T Y C N E U Q E R F B N O
P H S U O N O T O N O M A D L
P O T S I N U S G O L F N E D
A N C A T H U N D E R A G R D
R E I E L Z T R E H D O H C E
I S N S I K D E D E C I B E L
```

- ACOUSTICS
- APPLAUSE
- BANG
- BLAST
- BURST
- CHANGE
- DEAF
- DECIBEL
- DOMINANT TONE
- EARDRUM
- ECHO
- ELECTRONICS
- FREQUENCY
- GONG
- HEADPHONES
- HEARING IMPAIRED
- HERTZ
- INSTRUMENT
- LOW
- MONOTONOUS
- MUFFLE
- NOISE
- REPEAT
- SHRILL
- SONG
- SOURCE
- SPEED
- SPURT
- STEREO
- TALK
- THRESHOLD
- THUNDER

Film Quotes 1

ACROSS

1 A piece
5 Paperwork
10 Little row
14 Roman 1052
15 *The Emmys* author
16 Singer Arena
17 "You'll have only 'til midnight, and then ..." film
19 Noted 200-lap race
20 Renders irresistible
21 Bierce the cynic
23 Thistle-eater of kiddie lit
24 Muralist Chagall
25 World power in 1990
27 Cooks down, as a sauce
30 Mideast robes
33 Half-hearted
35 *True Colors* singer Collins
36 Return for one near the net
37 Cave denizen
38 *Odyssey* sea goddess
39 Clobber
41 Annoyed
43 Anne Sexton, e.g.
44 Like Nativity fliers
46 Red-tag event
48 Lattice piece
49 Groundhog
53 Purest Camelot knight
56 Jones of *Mad Men*
57 "This won't hurt ___!"
58 "The penguins are going, so why can't I?" film
60 Marcher's flute
61 Ditsy
62 Osprey's cousin
63 Chicken ___
64 Christened
65 *Lady and the Tramp*, e.g.

DOWN

1 Host a roast
2 1960s dress style
3 Model Crawford
4 Appalling
5 Jenny Gump's husband
6 Register fill
7 Divinity school subject: Abbr.
8 Kunis in *Ted*
9 Viciously insulted
10 It might help you get a leg up
11 "My nose! What's happened?" film
12 Added details
13 Diggs in *Chicago*
18 Dumbo's are jumbo
22 Michael Jackson album
26 Old violin
27 Confirmation et al.
28 Berlin article
29 Vending machine feature
30 Pierce player on *M*A*S*H*
31 "___ to Run": Springsteen
32 "You're lower than dirt. You're an ant!" film
34 Peace goddess
40 After the fact
41 Folic acid, for one
42 Like some returned goods
43 Gave the once-over
45 "Well, ___-di-dah"
47 Lang of Smallville
50 Close-up lens
51 Reddish tree dweller of Borneo
52 Reading radials
53 Large fishhook
54 He had an Irish Rose
55 Political commentator Perino
56 Judy Jetson's mom
59 Swing On, to Seabiscuit

BRAINSNACK® Fencing

Which posts (1–6) should replace the letters A, B and C?

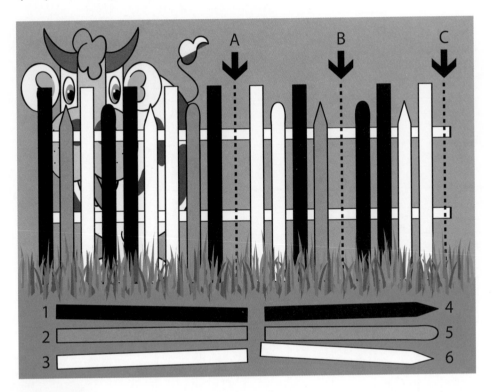

CLOCKWISE

The answers to the clues from 1 to 12 are all seven-letter words that end with the letter G. When you have solved the puzzle correctly, working clockwise from 1, the 12 letters in the outer circle will spell an abrupt word.

1 Covering up
2 Current
3 Obtrusive and persistent
4 Way in
5 Young tree
6 Open wide

7 Enduring
8 In want of
9 Moving at an easy pace
10 Illicit goods
11 Drooping loosely
12 Bringing to mind

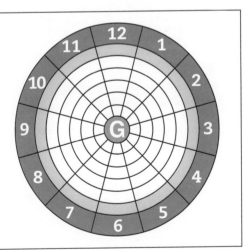

Sudoku X

Fill in the grid so that each row, each column, and each 3 x 3 frame contains every number from 1 to 9. The two main diagonals of the grid also contain every number from 1 to 9.

8								
				7		9	5	4
				4				1
1	7	3			5			
	8					5		
		4		5		2		
	5		2				9	
3	6			9	4		7	

do you KNOW

Where did Allied leaders meet in February 1945?

BLOCK ANAGRAM

Form the word that is described in the parentheses, using the letters above the grid. Extra letters are already in the right place.

CITY NEON (spiraling winds)

A				C		L		

TRIVIA QUIZ # Novel Ideas

Which did you like better, the book or the movie?
Here you get to think about books turned into movies.

1. Which 1991 movie has the same title as a 1986 novel by Anthony Powell?

   a. *The Fisher King*
   b. *From a View to a Death*
   c. *Afternoon Men*

2. Who did Sir Anthony Hopkins play in *Shadowlands?*

   a. J. R. R. Tolkien
   b. W. B. Yeats
   c. C. S. Lewis

3. On whose book was *The Name of the Rose* based?

   a. Stephen King
   b. John Updike
   c. Umberto Eco

4. Who wrote the novel *The Godfather,* on which the Mafia movies were based?

   a. Mario Puzo
   b. Francis Ford Coppola
   c. Gay Talese

5. The book *Enemy Coast Ahead* was adapted into which war film?

   a. *The Dam Busters*
   b. *Full Speed Ahead*
   c. *Damn the Torpedoes!*

6. Gregory Peck starred in *To Kill a Mockingbird*. Who wrote the best-selling book it was based on?

   a. Truman Capote
   b. Harper Lee
   c. Ralph Ellison

7. Dustin Hoffman starred as *The Graduate*. Who wrote the novel?

   a. Charles Webb
   b. Buck Henry
   c. Calder Willingham

8. Which novel by Kazuo Ishiguro became a 1993 movie starring Emma Thompson and Sir Anthony Hopkins?

   a. *The English Patient*
   b. *A Room with a View*
   c. *The Remains of the Day*

9. Which Thomas Hardy character was played by Nastassja Kinski in a 1979 movie?

   a. Lucy Honeychurch
   b. Tess of the D'Urbervilles
   c. Dorothea Brooke

trivia

• How many Harry Potter books were published, and how many movies were made from them?

_____

Rest Break

Enter the maze, pass over all WC signs from behind, and then exit.
You may not pass through a grid space more than once, and may not
enter a grid space in the line of a sign you have not yet passed over.

do you KNOW?

What vitamin
deficiency causes
scurvy?

THREE-IN-ONE

Using all of the letters listed below only once, can you find the names of three spices?

A A A C C D E G I M M M M N N N N O O R T U

CROSSWORD Film Quotes 2

ACROSS

1 Catch the scent of
6 Chevy in *Caddyshack*
11 Tachometer letters
14 Seminole rival
15 Snockered
16 Contemporary art?
17 "It means you're a baboon ... and I'm not." film
19 "___ the season ..."
20 Hustle, for one
21 Goliath gods
23 Hellhole
26 ___ Gritty Dirt Band
27 Vast emptiness
28 ___ *Italien*: Strauss
30 Word form for "field"
31 Reinking of *Chicago*
32 Meter maid of song
34 Continental coin
37 Sparks and Beatty
39 No longer in bed
40 Withers
41 Global land mass
42 Show elation
43 Ballet's Le ___ des Cygnes
44 Pheasant nest
46 Baseball stat
48 Utah ski spot
49 Hidden agenda
51 Hazy
53 Perceptive faculties
55 Neat collection
56 Speed
57 "Say hello to the Scream Extractor." film
62 Nightmarish street
63 Inspiration for Sappho
64 Thoreau work
65 ___-Pitch softball
66 Matt in *We Bought a Zoo*
67 No longer in

DOWN

1 USAF rank
2 Shania Twain hit
3 Relative of -arian
4 Threw in a hand
5 Monastery man
6 Park gathering area
7 Walk on trails
8 "Thrilla in Manila" boxer
9 Romantically wowed
10 Border adrornment
11 "... a tiny chef who tells me what to do." film
12 Send to press
13 In a shambles
18 Choreographer White
22 Drowsy
23 Eric Trump's mother
24 Canonical hour
25 "All drains lead to the ocean, kid." film
29 Eastern lute
30 Interlaken river
33 *Alice in Wonderland* director
35 Edna Ferber ranch
36 Award for *The Artist*
38 Windjammer features
39 Grampa Simpson
45 Judged to be
47 Memo words
48 Milano of *Who's the Boss?*
49 Barbecue remnants
50 Sam in *Alcatraz*
52 Minded
54 Small marsh bird
55 Regarding
58 Skater Naomi Nari ___
59 Suffix for violin
60 Scots negative
61 Charisse in *Brigadoon*

Big-Nosed Bornean

ACROSS

1 Price tag
5 Improves a road
10 Fast-talking
14 Where Navajo Mountain is located
15 Breathing
16 ___ avis (nonpareil)
17 Wash
18 Passover feast
19 Native of Mecca
20 Long-nosed monkey
23 Dawn goddess
24 Geisha's sash
25 Berra of baseball
27 Former •
31 Minus
34 Organic compound
36 "The Tortoise and the Hare" author
37 Paris water
38 Largest living bird
40 Father of Phineas
41 A surcoat covers it
43 Speak wildly
44 Bric-a-___
45 Hollywood site
47 Nobelist Wiesel
49 Celtic Neptune
50 Printing goofs
54 Binomial name of 20-Across
60 Leprechaun's land
61 One of the Judds
62 Smoke glass
63 Keep an eye on
64 Deadly Asian snake
65 Anon companion
66 Pudding starch
67 *Grease* heroine
68 Syringe fluids

DOWN

1 *Mea* ___ (my fault)
2 Hokkaido city
3 Relish
4 *For* ___ (1991 Midler movie)
5 Oceanic crossings
6 Guinness in *Murder by Death*
7 *Veni,* ___ , *vici*
8 Holiday nights
9 Pulpit talk
10 Countertop choice
11 Merry prank
12 *Dies* ___ (Latin hymn)
13 Justin Bieber hit
21 El Dorado treasure
22 West Indies sorcery
26 Prefix for mural
27 Nana Oyl's daughter
28 Elbe feeder
29 Ocean sunfish
30 Grandiose
31 Electric Nissan
32 English peer
33 Japanese sport
35 "... man ___ mouse?"
38 Projecting window
39 Rapidity
42 City near Disney World
44 Puts down
46 Manhattan et al.
48 Rap producer Gotti
51 Suffix for talk
52 Radio control
53 *Ad* ___ *per aspera* (Kansas motto)
54 Brooklyn team
55 Zone
56 Belt out
57 Errani of tennis
58 Bank offering
59 In the center

Sport Maze

Draw the shortest way from the ball to the goal. You can only move along vertical and horizontal lines, not along diagonal lines. The figure on each square indicates the number of squares the ball must move in the same direction. You can change direction at each stop.

3	1	5	4	3	2
5	2	4	2	1	5
5	4	3	1	1	5
1	2	3	2	0	4
1	3	1	4	1	4
●	2	5	2	1	2

trivia

- What is the sign of someone born on Halloween?

ONE LETTER LESS OR MORE

The word on the right side contains the letters of the word on the left side, plus or minus the letter in the middle. One letter is already in the right place.

WANDERER +U ☐ ☐ ☐ E ☐ ☐ ☐ ☐

Typist

Which letter in the last word TWSPUTWR will change to form the next word?

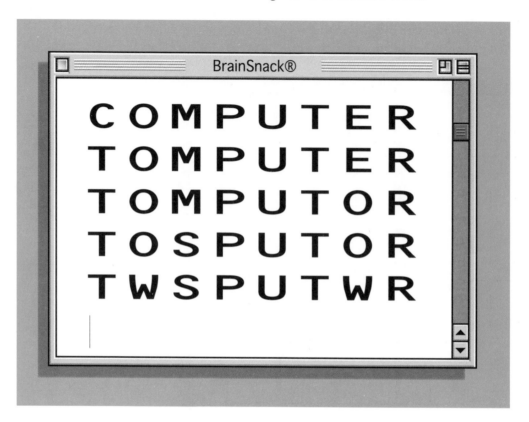

LETTER LINE

Put a letter in each of the squares below to make a word that is a sixteenth note.
The number clues refer to other words that can be made from the whole.

3 7 6 8 2 SHADE OF PURPLE • 1 5 6 4 10 3 TO WRIGGLE, WRITHE
2 7 8 9 1 PROJECTING EDGE OF A ROOF
10 2 5 6 4 9 3 MUSIC COMPOSED AS A MEMORIAL • 5 6 2 10 4 9 1 QUESTIONS

1	2	3	4	5	6	7	8	9	10

Word Sudoku

Complete the grid so that each row, each column, and each 3 x 3 frame contains the nine letters from the black box below. The hidden nine-letter word is in the diagonal from top left to bottom right.

A	B	G	I	L	N	O	R	U
				I				
					L		I	
O	A		G			I		
A					B			
	U	G						I
	N	B			R	L		
	L			A	U			O
N			L	R				B
		N	I					

do you KNOW?

Which spiral galaxy is closest to our own?

_____

Kakuro

Each number in a black area is the sum of the numbers that you have to enter in the next empty boxes. The empty boxes that make up the sum are called a run. The sum of the across run is written above the diagonal in the black area, and the sum of the down run is written below the diagonal. Runs can only contain the numbers 1 through 9, and each number in a run can only be used once. The gray boxes only contain odd numbers and the white only even numbers.

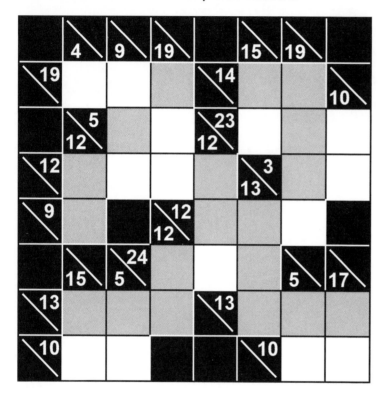

SANDWICH

What four-letter word belongs between the word at left and the word at right, so that the first and second word, and the second and third word, each form a common compound word or phrase?

DRIFT _ _ _ _ TURNER

CROSSWORD Themeless 6

ACROSS

1 Filtered mail
5 Cutpurse
10 Blanched
14 Headey of *Game of Thrones*
15 Teeming throng
16 Udometer measure
17 Concerned
19 Lunch-box cookie
20 Swamplands
21 Apprehensive
23 On the docket
24 Lay waste
25 Dust cloths
27 Prada product
30 Rounds in a fight?
33 Leaded gas
35 Large kangaroo
36 Arthur or Lillie
37 Drive away
38 Umbrella piece
39 Party popper
41 Camera lens
43 Make a novena
44 Todd of Fleet Street
46 Rug type
48 Short-runway plane
49 Crossword direction
53 Mint flavoring
56 Have a go at
57 German automaker
58 *The Devil's* ___: Bierce
60 ___ majesty
61 "What did ___ deserve this?"
62 Lanky
63 Rents out
64 *Washington Journal* channel
65 Stuffing herb

DOWN

1 Diets successfully
2 Punitive
3 Anatomical cavities
4 Conductor
5 U2 guitarist
6 *Bonanza* son
7 NYC's first subway line
8 Biblical garden
9 Union soldier
10 Supply
11 Thomas Jefferson's 1800 rival
12 "In ___ of flowers ..."
13 Father of Cainan
18 Mother of Zeus
22 *Cats* had a long one
26 Shepherd's concern
27 Monster slain by Hercules
28 Solo for Figaro
29 "As Tears ___": Rolling Stones
30 Kindergarten topic
31 Cat call
32 Hoax
34 Noise from a sot
40 Kitchen whistlers
41 Euphonious
42 Valedictory, e.g.
43 Curfew setters
45 Japanese drama
47 *Ghostbusters* car
50 City in Nebraska
51 Mistletoe piece
52 *Funny Girl* composer
53 Mobster's lady
54 Electric sword
55 Hats, slangily
56 "___ boy!"
59 Beat walker

Sudoku Twin

Fill in the grid so that each row, each column, and each 3 x 3 frame contains every number from 1 to 9. A sudoku twin is two connected 9 x 9 sudokus.

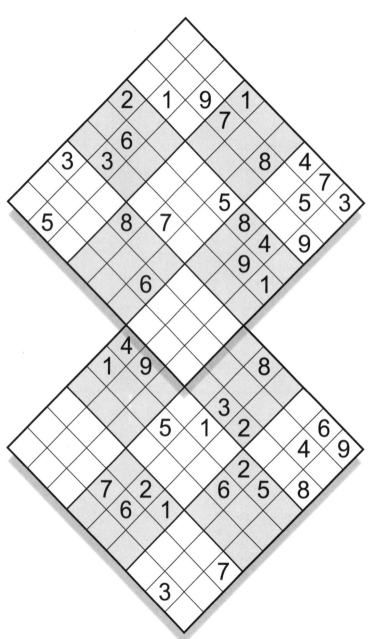

BRAINSNACK® In Balance

Which weight (A-D) should replace the question mark so that the scale is in balance?

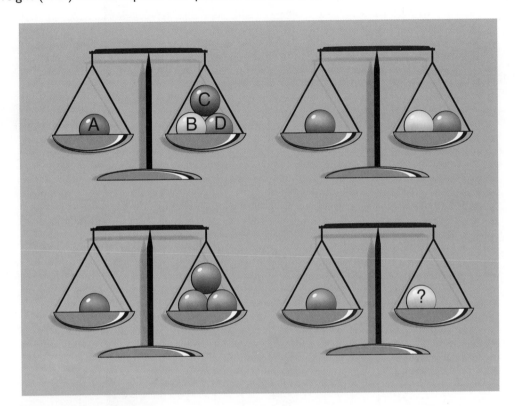

QUICK CROSSWORD

Place the sport-related words listed below in the crossword grid.

LAST JUDO HELMET GOLD YACHT SHOE NETBALL JAIALAI WIN

From Acorn to Tree

ACROSS

1 Light rain
5 Sword fights
10 Diner "sugar"
14 Rectangular pilaster
15 Sundance film
16 Plains tribesman
17 Start of a Word Ladder: ACORN ___
20 1972 Olympics site
21 Not always
22 Nuptial response
23 Tint or tone
24 Spas
28 Administrative headache
32 Of yore
33 Rental agreement
35 *Salome* selection
36 Word Ladder continues
40 Notify
41 8th Greek letter
42 Bishopric
43 Insists upon
46 Generous bestowal
48 "Boy, am I dumb!"
49 Moo ___ gai pan
50 Orbital points
54 No longer in use
58 End of a Word Ladder: ___ TREES
60 Level a structure
61 Student getting one-on-one help
62 Art style of the 1920s
63 Cash-register stack
64 Stylish
65 Poll conclusion?

DOWN

1 M, to Einstein
2 Member of a bygone empire
3 "Freeze!"
4 La Brea attraction
5 Takes it all off
6 "Address to the ___ Guid": Burns
7 Old Tokyo
8 San Marino coin, formerly
9 Burn up
10 Communal
11 Scintilla
12 Slangy denial
13 Not-so-hot grades
18 Small knot
19 Kind of poker
24 "___ luego!"
25 Is all leers
26 Utensils
27 Casa rooms
28 Stave off
29 "Kiss From ___": Seal
30 Components of some organs
31 Relieves pressure
34 Our star
37 Pawnbrokers, e.g.
38 Mise en scène
39 Way out there
44 Has regrets
45 Pilferages
47 Pumpkin relatives
50 Hendrix hairdo
51 Intend
52 Soft mud
53 Urban eyesore
54 Venison
55 Without a mixer
56 Hand over (to)
57 Nicholas I, e.g.
59 7th Greek letter

WORD POWER ▸ Zoo Logic

A real safari may be out of reach, but you can still talk about the
animal kingdom like a seasoned guide. Explore this menagerie of words
and then scout for answers.

. . . .

1. **fauna** ('faw-nuh) *n.*—
   A: baby deer. B: beast of myth.
   C: animal life in a region.

2. **nicker** ('ni-ker) *v.*—
   A: chirp like a cricket.
   B: chatter like a chimp.
   C: whinny like a horse.

3. **savanna** ('suh-van-ah) *n.*—
   A: grassland. B: paper fan.
   C: tall cabinet.

4. **nocturnal** ('noc-tur-nal) *adj.*—
   A: fast moving. B: without legs.
   C: active at night.

5. **vulpine** ('vul-piyn) *adj.*—
   A: like a wolf. B: like a fox.
   C: like a crow.

6. **flews** ('flooz) *n.*—
   A: swarms of midges.
   B: cuckoo nests. C: droopy lips,
   like a bloodhound's.

7. **aquiline** ('a-kwi-liyn) *adj.*—
   A: resembling an eagle's beak.
   B: living in the sea.
   C: warm-blooded.

8. **piebald** ('piy-bald) *adj.*—
   A: hairless. B: spotted. C: scaly.

9. **headwater** ('hed-water) *n.*—
   A: source of a stream.
   B: head rush caused by warmer
   temperatures.
   C: current running along a boat.

10. **clutch** ('kluch) *n.*—
    A: forepaw. B: nest of eggs.
    C: predator's quarry.

11. **tawny** ('taw-nee) *adj.*—
    A: of a warm sandy color.
    B: having talons.
    C: with soft feathers.

12. **prehensile** (pree-'hen-suhl)
    adj.—A: adapted for grasping.
    B: developed in an eggshell.
    C: eats insects.

13. **estivate** ('es-ti-vayt) *v.*—
    A: store water as camels do.
    B: change habitats.
    C: sleep through the summer.

14. **territorial** ('ter-ri-tor-ee-ul)
    adj.—A: like a terrier.
    B: relating to a specific area.
    C: having an ability to swim.

15. **polecat** ('pohl-kat) *n.*—
    A: mountain lion.
    B: Arctic hare. C: skunk.

WORD SEARCH Dreams

All the words are hidden vertically, horizontally, or diagonally—in both directions. The letters that remain unused form a sentence from left to right.

```
S U D D E N N I G H T M A R E
D R R E B A E F R E Q U E N T
M I E N G R K I S E U G A V O
S C E P F T A E N T S W E A T
L O D E R C W I M A G I N E O
E N A R M E A P N L F E A R T
E F F S A N S W E R S A R I C
P U E P L E A S A N T D B T I
W S D I R O N F I H A A L L D
A I U R E E F J U O H C I U E
L N E E M O H N O A N H O T R
K G R I E N E T G Y I L S S P
I O F Z M M G E A N A U T I M
N E O S B P N E D E O B O P L
G D E C E A A E N I R E L V E
R U C E R N R F R L Y B I E N
C H A R A C T E R T H E B E D
I R D M E S S A G E R E A M S
```

■ ANSWERS	■ LOUD
■ AWAKEN	■ MESSAGE
■ BED	■ NIGHTMARE
■ BRAIN	■ PERSPIRE
■ BREATHE	■ PLEASANT
■ CHARACTER	■ PREDICT
■ CONFUSING	■ RECUR
■ DOZE OFF	■ REMEMBER
■ ENJOYABLE	■ REPRESSION
■ FADE	■ SERIOUS
■ FEAR	■ SLEEPWALKING
■ FREQUENT	■ STRANGE
■ FREUD	■ SUDDEN
■ HABIT	■ SWEAT
■ HINDER	■ VAGUE
■ IMAGINE	
■ LATE	

168

Do the Math

Enter numbers in each row and column to arrive at the end totals.
Numbers must be from 1 to 9 and used only once.

	+		−		=	4
+		+		−		
	−		+		=	4
+		−		+		
	+		−		=	3
=		=		=		
16		13		10		

trivia

- Regan MacNeil is a character in which 1973 film?

Retronyms 1

ACROSS

1 Femme's husband
5 Eckhart in *Erin Brockovich*
10 Imperial leader of yore
14 Guinness in *Lawrence of Arabia*
15 Russell in *Robin Hood*
16 Ancient Cuzco citizen
17 Not a talkie
19 Draped wear of Delhi
20 H.M.S. *Pinafore* extras
21 Time in court
23 Emulate Houdini
24 David's father-in-law
25 Loch near Inverness
27 Movie houses
30 Beyond suggestive
33 Practices punching
35 2010 Angelina Jolie film
36 Cigar dropping
37 Tow truck summoner
38 Dockers' gp.
39 Bard
41 *Miss Saigon* hero
43 Go like a hummingbird
44 Brat
46 *La Strada* composer Rota
48 Join the workforce
49 Retail minus cost
53 Womanizers, slangily
56 Make nice with
57 Essayist Lamb
58 Not shades
60 Get mushy
61 Saw logs
62 "Take ___!"
63 Elbow
64 José Carreras, for one
65 Lip disservice

DOWN

1 Shot by Minnesota Fats
2 False handle
3 Dig treasure
4 Where Fischer beat Spassky in 1972
5 Play girl?
6 Barks in strips
7 King, to Henri
8 Fifth-year exams at Hogwarts
9 Archenemy
10 Sniffler's boxful
11 Non-electronic messages
12 Phobia start
13 Cause of slick streets
18 "Not a chance!"
22 ___ Marino
26 1957 Cy Young winner
27 Jeanne in *State Fair*
28 "___ Know": Garfunkel
29 "On the double!"
30 Place for mascara
31 Suffix for coal
32 Alternative to skim
34 River at Bern
40 Soothe
41 Challenge a will
42 Less convoluted
43 Black and Sherwood
45 Lyricist Gershwin
47 Valley near San Francisco
50 Buckwheat dish
51 "___ directed"
52 Raid targets
53 Non-permanent employee
54 Muffin topper
55 "... for auld lang ___"
56 Word form for "soil"
59 Many millennia

Futoshiki

Fill in the 5 x 5 grid with the numbers from 1 to 5 once per row and column, while following the greater-than/lesser-than symbols shown. There is only one valid solution that can be reached through logic and clear thinking alone!

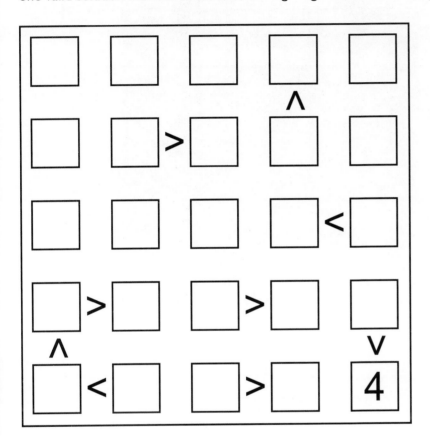

The word "Kitsch" is derived from which language?

TRIANAGRAM

Three-word groups of anagrams are also called triplets or trianagrams.
Complete the group:

D E S E R T _ _ _ _ _ _   _ _ _ _ _ _

Celebration

Which letter is made up of the wrong confetti?

QUICK WORD SEARCH

Find the musical terms listed below in the word search grid.

S	O	P	R	A	N	O	W	Q	U	I	N	T	E	T
H	M	R	H	A	R	M	O	N	Y	S	L	I	D	E
A	Z	O	Y	E	S	I	R	P	E	R	M	W	U	M
R	F	O	R	M	A	E	S	T	R	O	M	O	T	P
P	R	E	L	U	D	E	O	T	A	G	E	L	E	O

**ETUDE FORM HARMONY LEGATO MAESTRO PRELUDE QUINTET
REPRISE SHARP SLIDE SOPRANO TEMPO**

CROSSWORD Retronyms 2

ACROSS

1 Trim back
5 Keep from acting
10 P&L preparers
14 "The end ___ era"
15 Japanese beer or city
16 *Ugly Betty* actor Michael
17 Alternative to animated
19 Mine vein
20 Recluse
21 Lost it
23 1994 *Frankenstein* star
24 Bat Masterson's friend
25 Strange
27 Was behind
30 Father of the Reo
33 Hera's birthplace
35 Yarn
36 Chou En-___
37 Tide type
38 Long in *Boiler Room*
39 Show horse
41 Toweled off
43 ___ *Flux* (Theron film)
44 Harper of *Rhoda*
46 An arm or a leg
48 Added bonus
49 Dude ranch activity
53 Advises earnestly
56 Roll-on alternative
57 Links club
58 Kodak Brownie, for one
60 Summoned staff, in a way
61 Eastern Christian
62 Times to remember
63 "Bette Davis ___": Kim Carnes
64 Yorkshire city
65 Flanders and Kelly

DOWN

1 Punted, in a sense
2 Ablaze
3 Poe bird
4 More than just rivals
5 *House* roles
6 Suffix akin to -kin
7 ___ Lung in *Kung Fu Panda*
8 Youngest Greek god
9 Snowmobile skis
10 Perpetrator
11 Jet forerunner
12 Coadjutant
13 Provide with startup capital
18 River flowing through Leeds
22 Highway help org.
26 Bulldog of New Haven
27 Poolside turban
28 Chacon of the 1962 Mets
29 James in *East of Eden*
30 Former king of Norway
31 Superman's mom
32 Touch-Tone predecessor
34 Do a floor chore
40 Fits in
41 Full of yearning
42 Calls the shots?
43 Midsection
45 Classic robot play
47 Sorvino in *Summer of Sam*
50 River past Grenoble
51 Org. that "tracks" Santa
52 *Einstein on the Beach* composer
53 Waterford locale
54 Superman's vision
55 ___ qua non
56 *Diary of ___ Housewife* (1970)
59 Equivocate

Figure 8's

These are the skating details that every figure skater and true enthusiast must know.
Can you spot the right answer to the following questions?

1. In this jump, the takeoff is on a forward outside edge, and then the skater makes one and a half revolutions in the air and lands on the other foot on a back outside edge. Name that jump.

   a. Axel jump
   b. Lutz
   c. Salchow

2. Name the jump in which the skater stops briefly with one foot extended behind, then swings that leg forward and around with a wide scooping motion, before landing backward on the foot and leg that performed the scooping motion.

   a. An axel jump
   b. Lutz
   c. Salchow

3. This star of the 1976 Olympics also had a hairstyle that was copied by young girls everywhere.

   a. Dorothy Hamill
   b. Peggy Fleming
   c. Michelle Kwan

4. Skating is believed to have originated in Scandinavia around 1000 BC. The earliest-known skates were strapped to the bottom of the foot and used what material for the blade?

   a. Metal
   b. Bone
   c. Stone

5. When did the International Skating Union eliminate from competition the compulsory section, in which prescribed figures were traced?

   a. 1970
   b. 1950
   c. 1990

6. In Olympic figure skating, what type of music are skaters not allowed to use in their routine?

   a. Rock music
   b. Music with vocals
   c. Jazz

7. Where was American world champion Sonja Henie born?

   a. Oslo, Norway
   b. Oswego, New York
   c. Ottawa, Canada

8. What happened to the U.S. figure skating team in 1961?

   a. They were involved in a doping scandal.
   b. They were killed in a plane crash.
   c. They won every event in which they competed.

9. For which country did Katarina Witt compete?

   a. East Germany
   b. Austria
   c. United States

Find the Right Word

Knowing that every arrow points to a letter and that no letter can touch another vertically, horizontally, or diagonally, find the missing letters that form a key word in reading direction. A letter cannot be located on an arrow. We show one letter in a circle to help you get started.

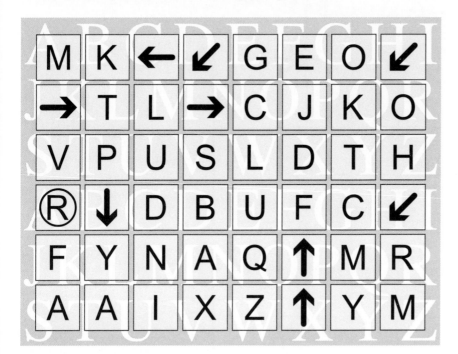

do you KNOW?

Which artist had a Blue Period?

CHANGELINGS

Each of the three lines of letters below spell the names of musical instruments, but the letters have been mixed up. Four letters from the first word are now in the third line, four letters from the third word are in the second line, and four letters from the second word are in the first line. The remaining letters are in their original places. What are the words?

D	I	T	B	E	U	I	D	O	E
O	A	M	S	O	H	R	I	N	N
S	D	U	G	A	P	R	O	O	E

Sudoku

Fill in the grid so that each row, each column, and each 3 x 3 frame contains every number from 1 to 9.

				7		1		
	5						9	
					5			4
	4						1	7
								8
5		8	6					2
3				8	7			
	6	2	9				7	
9			3				4	

do you KNOW?

What is the capital of Indonesia?

176

SYMBOL SUMS

Can you work out these number sums using three of these four symbols? **+ − ÷ ×**

12 ☐ 8 ☐ 13 ☐ 4 = 13

Graffiti

Enter the maze, pass over all graffiti paint cans from behind (thereby catching them), and then exit. You may not pass through a grid space more than once, and may not enter a grid space in the line of a paint can you have not yet caught.

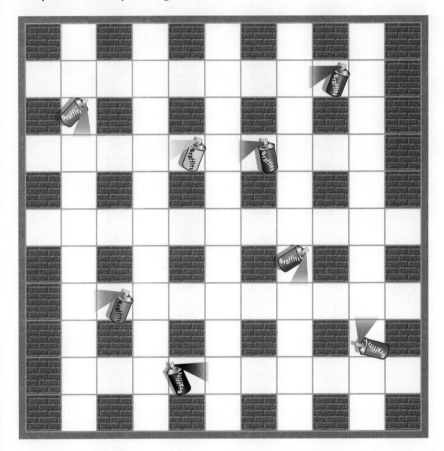

trivia

- Who was Fred Astaire's famous dancing partner?

_____

FRIENDS

What do the following words have in common?

BOSS DECOY DOMINEER LANDSCAPE MANIKIN WAFFLE YACHT

Dynamic Duos

ACROSS

1 Bottom half of *Laugh-In* duo, with 30 down
5 Bottom half of "Who's on First" duo, with 11 down
10 Possess
12 R2-D2 for one
13 Jerry's ice cream partner
14 Disney canine sidekick to 23 down
16 Beloved doll's boyfriend
17 Ancient board game
18 Smarter half of a detective duo, with 51 across
19 Shade of black
20 Goes with Capitan
22 Thanksgiving veggie
24 Captivate
27 Hawaiian singer Don
28 "Of the" in France
29 Game show host _____ Barker
30 Flying squirrel in zany 1960s cartoon duo, with 40 across
32 Caped crusader
34 Like a bairn
35 Bottom half of comedy duo (pictured)
36 "Mamma Mia" group
38 In forms, abbreviation that means "doesn't apply"
40 Goofy moose half of cartoon duo, with 30 across
44 West of *My Little Chickadee*
46 Raw iron
47 Arts degree
48 "I did it _____ way," from Frank Sinatra's big hit

49 Bad half of 19 down
50 "Stand _____ me"
51 Half of a detective duo, with 18 across

DOWN

1 Rival to Avon, 2 words
2 Partner to 32 across
3 Duo's number
4 "Off we go _____ the wild blue yonder"
6 Wine: Prefix
7 Style of dance
8 Skinny half of silent-era duo, with 33 down
9 Reed instrument
11 Top half of "Who's on First" duo, with 5 across
15 Piña _____
17 Military title (abbr.)
18 Lyndon Johnson's dog
19 Good half of horror duo, with 49 across
21 Paid task
23 Big-eared friend to 14 across
25 50th state (abbr.)
26 String instrument
27 Endearment short form

29 She's dating 16 across
30 Top half of *Laugh-In* duo, with 1 across
31 Necklaces, rings and other fine things
32 Operatic villains, often
33 Portly half of silent-era duo, with 8 down
37 Three-player card game
39 One of Jo's sisters
40 Spelling contest
41 Tennis shot
42 _____, the people
43 Hoops grp.
45 TV commercial
48 Twin Cities' st.

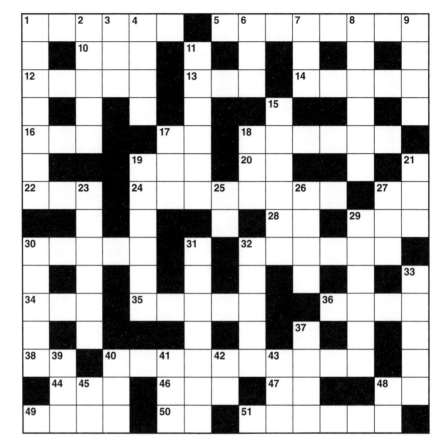

Word Ladders

Convert the word at the top of the ladders into the word at the bottom, using all the rungs in between. On each rung, you must put a valid word that has the same letters as the word above it, apart from one letter change. There may be more than one way to achieve this.

LASER

BEAMS

WATER

FALLS

BRAINSNACK® Shapely

Which shape (1–6) should replace the question mark?

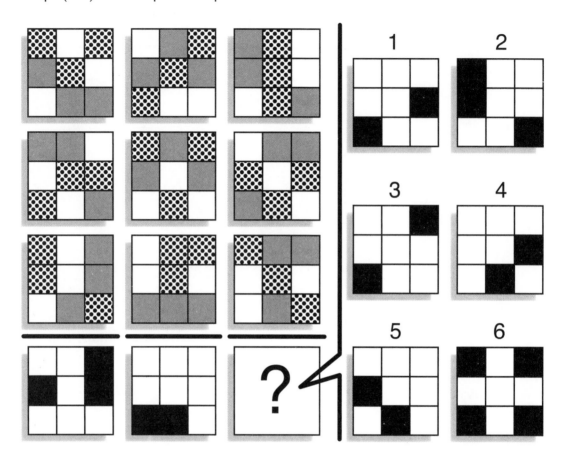

1

2

3

4

5

6

DOODLE PUZZLE

A doodle puzzle is a combination of images, letters, and/or numbers that represent a word or a concept. If you cannot solve a doodle puzzle, do not look at the answer right away. Think hard—and outside the box.

CROSSWORD # Freshen Up

ACROSS

1 "Dancing Queen" group
5 Bengay targets
10 "A" in radio lingo
14 Give notice
15 Computer order
16 Shakespearean king
17 Al Pacino on the stage: Part I
20 Tavern chair
21 To the same degree
22 City S of Moscow
24 Triplet
25 Al Pacino ...: Part II
30 *The Trip to Bountiful* author
31 Glass marble
32 Mothering
34 A-ha's "Take ___"
35 Irish premier De Valera
36 ___ *Lap* (1983 film)
37 *Great Expectations* hero
38 Initial stage
39 Uncool
40 Al Pacino ...: Part III
43 MacGraw and Baba
44 Korean border river.
45 Scout's mission
47 Majorca mister
50 Al Pacino ...: Part IV
55 Convertiplane
56 Witchy meeting
57 Protected from the wind
58 Spice up wine
59 Sonata movement
60 Bean in *GoldenEye*

DOWN

1 "How adorable!"
2 Disgruntled snorts
3 Singer Michaels
4 Make explanatory comments
5 Twin of Artemis
6 Grand ___ vineyard
7 Sot's comment
8 Brian of Roxy Music
9 One of the Leeward Islands
10 Pink-eyed animal
11 Unofficial news source
12 Facade
13 Deluge refuge
18 "___ Sixteen": Starr
19 Skip a syllable
23 Batman and Robin, e.g.
24 Rev. Lovejoy of *The Simpsons*
25 Pick-me-up
26 Je ne sais quoi
27 M. ___ Walsh of *Blade Runner*
28 Old anesthetic
29 Quench
30 Coxcomb
33 Shed a tear
35 Mastermind
36 Funnel-shaped flowers
38 Not at full power
39 Greek physician
41 Remote battery
42 Hair tune "___ Be Hard"
45 Intro to VW
46 Tautomeric compound
48 Look impolitely
49 Bird with three toes
50 Doctrine
51 Brandy label letters
52 Opposite of WbS
53 "Tubular!"
54 Bo Derek comedy

Language Quirks 1

ACROSS

1 Hotel amenities
5 Piece of broccoli
10 Shoulder wraps
14 Russell in *Overboard*
15 Party-giver Mesta
16 Oilman Halliburton
17 Certain plaintiff, at law
18 Insurance scheme
19 At large
20 What the wacko was during grilling?
23 Yuletide libation
24 Clock numeral
25 Fishy groups
29 Daughter of Leto
33 Stevedore's org.: Abbr.
34 Breakfast fruit
36 Helen's *Waterworld* friend
37 Bonnie girl
39 Lorna ___ cookies
41 Sign of rain
42 Daisy relative
44 "___ Eyes": The Guess Who
46 North Carolina river
47 Rome's ___ Steps
49 Star-studded
51 Fort Worth college
52 Furor
53 San Antonio's current hoop star?
62 Collette in *Little Miss Sunshine*
63 Animals, collectively
64 Musophobiac's fear
65 *Vissi d'___*: Puccini
66 Rye disease
67 ___ even keel
68 Some Ali wins
69 Witherspoon in *This Means War*
70 Straight up

DOWN

1 Arctic bird
2 Word on a door
3 Code type
4 Jelly fuel
5 Decorated with sequins
6 El Misti locale
7 While lead-in
8 "Thanks ___!"
9 "The Bathers" painter
10 Cozy up to
11 Odd, in Oban
12 Guinness who played Obi-Wan
13 Try to track down
21 Toontown judge
22 Make a reference to
25 George Eliot's Marner
26 Grip tightly
27 "___ luego!"
28 Lethargy
29 Queen ___ lace
30 Sponge mushroom
31 Massey in *Rosalie*
32 Rich flavor
35 "How impressive!"
38 Lookout men
40 Calculate approximately
43 *Hannah Montana* character
45 Eliel's designing son
48 Do more than abide
50 Jack in *The China Syndrome*
53 Hospital imperative
54 Political handouts
55 "Thy word is a lamp ___ my feet"
56 Weight not charged for
57 Titanic
58 Nephew of Abel
59 A, to Albrecht
60 Campus sports org.
61 Safari shelter

Umbrella Trouble

A math teacher bought an umbrella that, when unfolded, looked like this from above. Can you help identify the missing number on the umbrella?

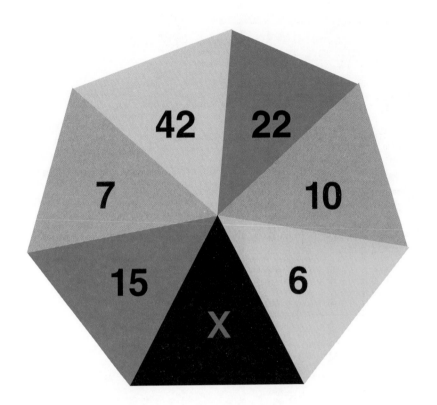

trivia

- Who was Marie Antoinette married to?

_____

Put a letter in each of the squares below to make a word which means relationship
The number clues refer to other words that can be made from the whole.

4 1 2 6 2 WATERING HOLE • 5 10 9 11 3 LOOSE CHANGE •
5 1 2 9 11 10 GAMBLING HOUSE • 1 5 8 9 4 11 DEED • 5 4 1 2 8 EDGE

1	2	3	4	5	6	7	8	9	10

Sport Maze

Draw the shortest way from the ball to the goal. You can only move along vertical and horizontal lines, not along diagonal lines. The figure on each square indicates the number of squares the ball must move in the same direction. You can change direction at each stop.

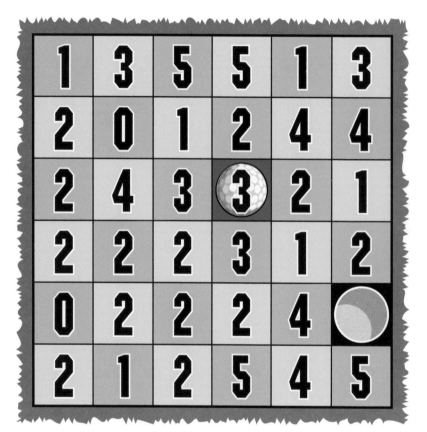

do you **KNOW**

Which play revolves around the Salem witch trials?

ONE LETTER LESS OR MORE

The word on the right side contains the letters of the word on the left side, plus or minus the letter in the middle. One letter is already in the right place.

E M I G R A N T +H [ ] I [ ] [ ] [ ] [ ] [ ] [ ]

WORD SEARCH · Magic

All the words are hidden vertically, horizontally, or diagonally—in both directions. The letters that remain unused form a sentence from left to right.

```
T S H S E E V E W O R C D M N
T U O P S G A T R O F I T E I
C O O E S R N U N I U R N D F
A R L C T S I I D E F C I O F
R E E T R D S N T I O U A V O
E T V A E W H H I I E S H E C
T X I T E E N P N D C N C S D
A E T O T R E S R F U X C E O
W D A R R C I C M I N O E E N
R G T S M L A N A G I P H O S
E A E C E I P T G R S H O W I
D R B N I M O C K S D L S I S
N S A B U A D N D O L S U S O
U C B T I X I E D A L Y T E N
E T H E I T U N B C A A N C P
T P A T I O M N A B G R A R Y
C H A R L A T A N E C A D E H
A B R C A S S I S T A N T T A
```

- ART
- ASSISTANT
- AUDIENCE
- BALLOON
- CANE
- CAPE
- CARDS
- CHAIN
- CHARLATAN
- CIRCUS
- CLIMAX
- COFFIN
- COINS
- DEXTEROUS
- DOVES
- EXCITING
- FIRE
- HOUDINI
- HYPNOSIS
- LEVITATE
- PODIUM
- RABBIT
- RINGS
- ROPE
- SECRET
- SHOW
- SPECTATORS
- SPEED
- STAGE
- STREET
- UNDERWATER ACT
- VANISH

Language Quirks 2

ACROSS

1 Donkey's cry
5 Cat Nation people
10 Gift label word
14 The Kinks hit of 1970
15 *The Addams Family* butler
16 Decor change
17 Church corner
18 *The Wreck of the Mary ___* (1959)
19 *Idylls of the King* lady
20 Where the stumped puzzle solver went?
23 Malleus locale
24 Steak seasoning
25 Weapons stash
29 Clothes with slogans
33 Set a match to
34 Drama coach Stella
36 Witherspoon in *Walk the Line*
37 Rapper born Tracy Marrow
39 Caravan stops
41 Penn in *Fair Game*
42 Hectare's 2.47
44 Selena's *Hotel Transylvania* role
46 No and Who
47 Rat Pack leader
49 Dead end
51 Full deck at Caesar's palace?
52 CCC x IV
53 Not well, in a "Morton Salt Girl" sense?
62 Manolete's opponent
63 Long-snouted browser
64 Move like mud
65 Carolina college town
66 Rousseau classic
67 Little League stats
68 Alan Arkin film
69 Was in a heat
70 Chimney sight

DOWN

1 Tell all
2 Italia capital
3 Baldwin in *Beetlejuice*
4 Union soldier
5 City of fabled riches
6 Regrets
7 Mesopotamia today
8 Hose shade
9 Fleeces
10 They're on the house
11 Nevada border city
12 Supreme Norse deity
13 Method
21 Blue Nile source
22 Steel-producing valley
25 False identity
26 Christina in *Speed Racer*
27 Rudder locale
28 Andean animal
29 Fountain of 2-Down
30 Oboe inserts
31 Russian dynasts
32 Touch, for one
35 Spanish pronoun
38 *Jurassic Park III* star
40 Boiled gently
43 Recipe directive
45 Humane org.
48 John of *Three's Company*
50 SAG members
53 El Paso school
54 No contest, briefly
55 Knock down
56 Syrian city
57 Cast-of-thousands
58 Artifice
59 Bindlestiff
60 Italian basso Pinza
61 Chill out

Word Sudoku

Complete the grid so that each row, each column, and each 3 x 3 frame contains the nine letters from the black box below. The hidden nine-letter word is in the diagonal from top left to bottom right.

A C E G L O R T W

C				O				W
W		E				G		
	L	R						
	E		C	W				A
	A				G	R		
R								
	C							
	A				L	T	G	
O			T			W		

do you KNOW?

In which country did Taekwando originate in?

UNCANNY TURN

Rearrange the letters of the phrase below to form a cognate anagram, one that is related or connected in meaning to the original phrase. The answer can be one or more words.

NO NIGHT SKY REMINDER

Cage the Animals

Draw lines to completely divide up the grid into small squares, with exactly one animal per square. The squares should not overlap.

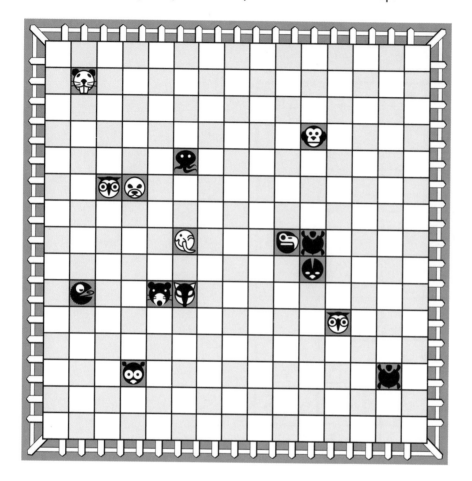

trivia

- Who directed the 1997 movie *Titanic*?

TRIVIAL PURSUIT Who Said That?

Words inspire as well as inform, especially during times of war.
Do you know which man or woman is associated with each of these famous quotes?

THE YEAR WAS 1942

1 "Now this is not the end. It is not even the beginning of the end. But perhaps it is the end of the beginning."

_____

2 "We are in a war and we need to fight it with all our ability and every weapon possible. Women pilots, in this particular case, are a weapon waiting to be used."

_____

3 "I'll come back as soon as I can with as much as I can. In the meantime, you've got to hold!"

_____

4 "The fruits of victory are tumbling into our mouths too quickly."

_____

5 "We shall attack and attack and attack until we are exhausted, and then we shall attack again."

_____

6 "That front is right here at home, in our daily lives, and in our daily tasks."

_____

7 "It seems to me that later on neither I nor anyone else will be interested in the musings of a 13-year-old schoolgirl."

_____

8 "We can do it!"

_____

trivia

- In 1942 many moviegoers were surprised to see what actor singing and dancing in the musical _Yankee Doodle Dandy?_

_____

Themeless 7

ACROSS

1 Chance on
5 Pageboy feature
10 Eight, in Seville
14 "Zip-___-Doo-Dah"
15 Reference marks
16 Do some food prep
17 Demotes
19 Swiss border river
20 Burr and Hamilton, e.g.
21 Without end
23 Single thread
24 Revise copy
25 Leeway
27 Nuclear fuel
30 Cabbie
33 Pepper grinders
35 ___ breve (cut time)
36 Musketeers motto word
37 *Dulce et decorum ___*: Horace
38 Sonny
39 Greeting from Simba
41 Toughen up
43 First to fly over the South Pole
44 Docent hirers
46 Gyroscope part
48 High-five
49 Conductor Boulez
53 iPhone features
56 Delivery from Cicero
57 Fashion's ___-Picone
58 Donald in *The Italian Job*
60 Latvian
61 Willis Tower, formerly
62 Opposite of ecto-
63 "___ bien!"
64 Flanges
65 Stash away

DOWN

1 Tires in the stretch
2 Shocking wedding response
3 More recent
4 Queen Margrethe II's country
5 Tedium
6 "Down with," in Dijon
7 Beatty in *Just Cause*
8 Euphoria
9 Sorority members
10 Ceramic aerophone
11 French lace
12 Circle dance
13 Ampera car company
18 Canadian singer Vannelli
22 Self-help author LeShan
26 Expressions
27 Excessive
28 Suffix for mod
29 Anti-DUI org.
30 Damage
31 Matty of baseball
32 Yearbook signer
34 Baton Rouge college
40 Lets up
41 Mexican standoff
42 State
43 Volkswagens
45 Alliance of 1958–61: Abbr.
47 "Pants on fire" guy
50 Happy as a lark
51 Classical musical form
52 What some wealthy alumni do
53 Boston cager, briefly
54 Declare
55 Went to court
56 German river
59 "It" game

Beady

Which color (1–6) should replace the bead with the question mark?

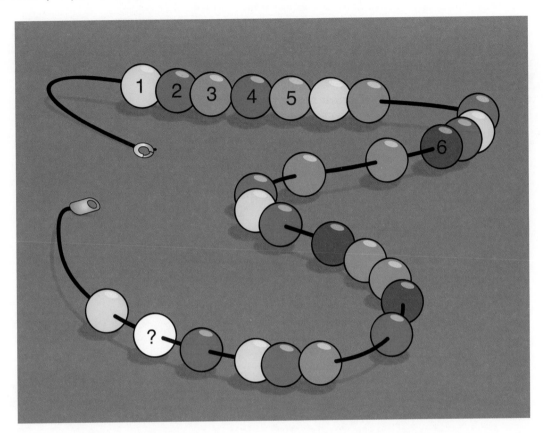

BLOCK ANAGRAM

Form the word that is described in the parentheses, using the letters above the grid. Extra letters are already in the right place.

NO GOLD (inundation of areas)

F _ _ _ I _ _

Piggybank Puzzles

In the currency peculiar to the country of Fennicia, 100 fents (the symbol for which is f) are equal to one Fennar (the symbol for which is F), so that one fennar + 28 fents is written as F1.28.

1. Using the pieces of money scattered around the money box below, fill the money box in such a way that each line of five small boxes (down, across, and diagonal) contains a sum total of F1.63. Some coins already have been placed in their correct boxes – just to give you a start.

2. Using the coins above the money box, fill it in such a way that each line of six small boxes (down, across, and diagonal) contains a total of F6.56.

Word Pyramid

Each word in the pyramid has the letters of the word above it, plus a new letter.

F
(1) note
(2) a great distance
(3) flat float
(4) later
(5) more quickly
(6) used to cut curved outlines
(7) computer programs

do you KNOW?

Which explorer
sailed on the *Niña*?

_____

_____

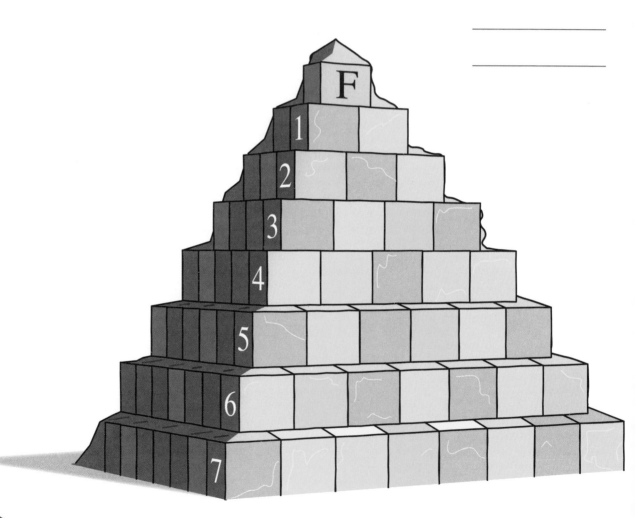

TRIVIA QUIZ **Governing Bodies**

How well versed are you in leadership issues? Take this test and find out!

1. In which ancient city did citizens practice ostracism, voting to expel politicians they disliked?

   a. Athens
   b. Rome
   c. Carthage

2. Whose national parliament from 1906 to 1917 was known as the Duma?

   a. Japan
   b. Sweden
   c. Russia

3. In which European country was there both a Long and a Rump parliament?

   a. England
   b. Portugal
   c. Germany

4. Which country has Europe's oldest lawmaking body, dating from 930?

   a. Iceland
   b. Poland
   c. Spain

5. Which Communist leader addressed the United Nations for over four hours in 1960?

   a. Nikita Khrushchev of the Soviet Union
   b. Mao Zedong of China
   c. Fidel Castro of Cuba

6. Which two European nations have the longest continuous treaty of friendship, signed in 1373?

   a. England and Portugal
   b. England and Switzerland
   c. Switzerland and Italy

7. Which Pacific kingdom claimed in 1976 to have the heaviest monarch at 463 pounds?

   a. Tonga
   b. Samoa
   c. Fiji

8. Which country has the oldest still-functioning written constitution?

   a. Greece
   b. United States
   c. Costa Rica

9. Which modern multinational executive body was headed by Jacques Delors until 1995?

   a. Amnesty International
   b. The European Commission
   c. The United Nations

Hourglass

Starting in the middle, each word in the top half has the letters of the word below it, plus a new letter, and each word in the bottom half has the letters of the word above it, plus a new letter.

(1) Expel, drive out

(2) Network of vessels in the body

(3) Beat

(4) Addition

(5) Stimulate

(6) Sweet sticky liquid

(7) Exatterated insistence on correctness

(8) Referees

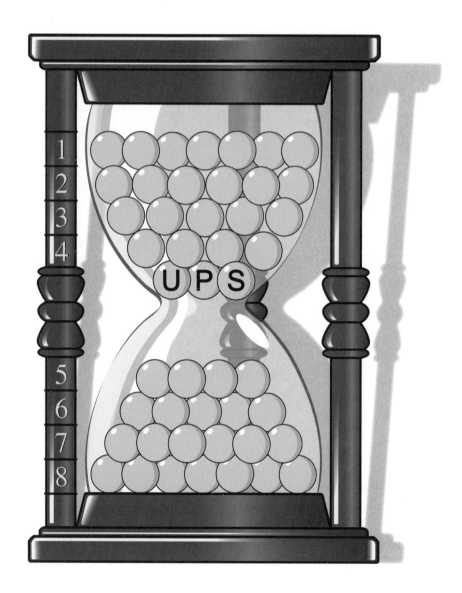

CROSSWORD Christmas Carols

ACROSS

1 Comprehensive test
5 Colombian city
9 Early internet service provider
12 Ceremonial room in Mesa Verde National Park
13 Old-time farm workers
14 Pontiac model
15 2, 4, 6 or 8, for example
16 "It Came Upon a ___ Clear"
18 You might flap them
20 Auf Wiedersehen
21 Calcutta mother
24 Directs a boat
25 When the moon hits your eye like a big pizza pie
26 Either guilty or not guilty
27 "The Little Drummer ___"
28 One-___ street
29 "___ to the World"
32 Word after vanity or state
34 Geologic feature of Norway
36 The gift that keeps on ___
39 Sioux and Hopi, for example
40 "Save me ___" (2 words)
41 Unpleasant feeling
42 "O Come All Ye ___"
44 Pesky bug
48 Shark's primary dorsal ___
49 *My Name Is* ___
50 Part of the ear
51 Actors Helms and O'Neill
52 Most famous mother
53 Paradise

DOWN

1 Squeeze (out)
2 14
3 5th, in NYC
4 "Away in a ___"
5 Pause in a sentence
6 What Earth spins on
7 Efficient bulb
8 Natural
9 Student in College Station, TX
10 .... by any ___ name
11 Aquatic flower
17 Notion
19 "___ your imagination"
21 Keyboard key
22 Introspective music
23 Cowboy Rogers
24 Tricky
26 Golf goal
28 Washington's was powdered
29 Work
30 Mineral deposit
31 Distances in football (abbr.)
32 Italian automobile
33 "O Canada" is one
34 Between Thu and Sat
35 "___ Bells"
36 Faux pas
37 "Was it something ___?" (2 words)
38 Blood vessels
39 Add up
41 Contented cat sound
43 Govt flight gp.
45 Show agreement
46 #16's nickname
47 Leaping lords

CROSSWORD — Play Ball

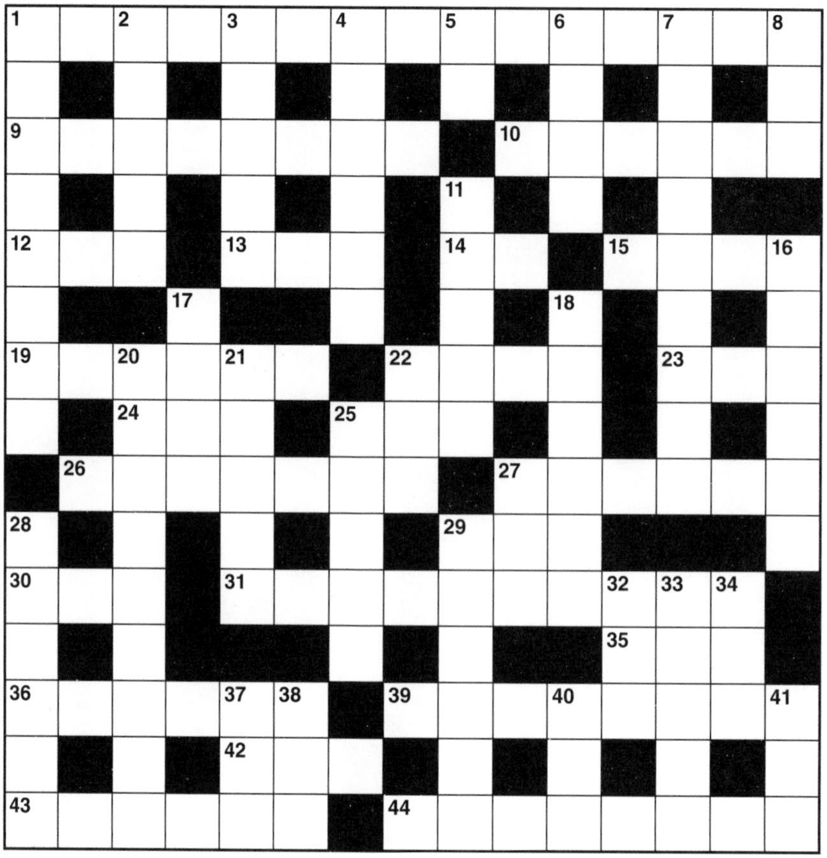

ACROSS

1 Joe Montana was a favorite at this classic California stadium, 2 words
9 Baltimore stadium called "The Old Gray Lady of 33rd Street"
10 Harry S's successor
12 He came in from the cold
13 Go on and on
14 _____ the money
15 English classic actor Guinness
19 Field named after a Dodgers' owner
22 Grounds where the Jets used to play
23 Lyric poem
24 Higher educational place for a Brit
25 _____-game show
26 Ivied field (pictured)
27 Batteries' positive terminals
29 Piece
30 Arden of Our Miss Brooks
31 Book that spawned a doll, 2 words
35 1960s sitcom couple Laura and _____ Petrie
36 Last name of the composer of "The Music of the Night"
39 The Rock, prison in San Francisco Bay
42 "That's tasty!"
43 "Sandman" was a much loved player at this classic New York ballpark
44 Bridge game opening, 2 words

DOWN

1 Chicago park where Joe Louis defeated James Braddock
2 Star Trek actor Leonard
3 Jim Croce's "Bad, Bad _____ Brown"
4 Ocean killers
5 "One _____ by land..."
6 Fuzzy-skinned fruit
7 Heavenly dessert? 2 words
8 First-aid box
11 Military action figure, 2 words
16 Dairy product
17 First of a Latin trio
18 Hank Aaron was a favorite at this classic Milwaukee stadium
20 It holds a stadium patty, 2 words
21 Classic stadium in Detroit nicknamed "The Corner"
22 Delve into
25 Skating medalist Fleming
27 Help
28 Boston park with a Green Monster
29 Cabaret setting
32 It's often left hanging
33 _____ Rae, 1979 drama
34 Golden State Nuggets' org.
37 Word with private or public
38 Parisian street
40 Wood used in baseball bats
41 Teen's embarrassment

The crossword grid with numbered cells is shown.

WORD POWER Good Sport

Test your gaming vocabulary with this playful quiz.
There's no harm, no foul, and no penalty for flipping to the answers.

. . . .

1. **aficionado** (uh-fish-ee-uh-'nah-doh) *n.*—A: referee. B: expert. C: buff.

2. **wheelhouse** ('weel-howse) *n.*— A: batter's ideal swinging range. B: overhand pitch. C: cycling stadium.

3. **laugher** ('laff-er) *n.*— A: close game. B: lopsided win. C: joker in a deck.

4. **gambit** ('gam-bit) *n.*— A: opening maneuver. B: single inning. C: intense rival.

5. **arbitrate** ('ahr-bi-trayt) *v.*— A: protest a call. B: serve as umpire. C: settle for a tie.

6. **chaff** ('chaf) *v.*—A: tease. B: discard. C: advance a pawn.

7. **thimblerig** ('thim-buhl-rig) *n.*— A: party platter. B: con game. C: handspring.

8. **see** ('see) *v.*— A: match, as a poker bet. B: leapfrog over. C: strike and open a piñata.

9. **ludic** ('loo-dik) *adj.*— A: following the rules. B: playful. C: easy to learn.

10. **baize** ('bayz) *n.*— A: pool-table fabric. B: long-range pass. C: sculling boat.

11. **maffick** ('maf-ik) *v.*— A: celebrate joyfully. B: enter a raffle. C: play solitaire.

12. **cat's game** ('kats 'gaym) *n.*— A: tie in tic-tac-toe. B: Parcheesi. C: yo-yo trick.

13. **token** ('toh-kin) *n.*— A: loss of a turn. B: signal to a partner. C: game piece.

14. **ruff** ('ruhf) *v.*— A: sail on a new tack. B: play a trump card. C: drive a ball off the fairway.

15. **hat trick** ('hat 'trik) *n.*— A: fancy outfield catch. B: three hockey goals by one player. C: "grand slam" of tennis.

Answers (Do You Know? and Trivia answers are on page 224)

Trophy Room

P	A	S	S		M	E	A	L	S		A	S	I	T
A	B	U	T		E	C	L	A	T		S	P	C	A
N	E	A	R		T	R	O	V	E		I	R	O	N
D	A	V	I	S	C	U	P		L	I	N	I	N	G
A	R	E	T	H	A				L	O	I	N		
			C	A	L	F		H	A	U	N	T	E	D
M	A	C	H		F	L	I	E	R			E	C	T	O
I	L	L				E	A	R			U	N	C	
L	E	A	D		T	E	N	D	S		C	P	A	S
A	E	R	A	T	E	S		S	T	A	R			
		E	Y	E	R				A	L	A	S	K	A
S	E	T	T	E	R		W	O	R	L	D	C	U	P
C	U	J	O		A	V	A	N	T		L	O	N	I
A	R	U	N		C	I	R	C	E		E	T	T	A
T	O	G	A		E	N	D	E	D		S	T	A	N

Play the Slots

Symbol 4. Join the beginning and the end of the strip to see the rest.

CLOCKWISE • EAVESDROPPER

1. EASTERN
2. ARTISAN
3. VENISON
4. EROSION
5. SAFFRON
6. DICTION
7. REFRAIN
8. ORATION
9. PELICAN
10. PARAGON
11. EARTHEN
12. RUBICON

The Christmas Movie

1. c. Bill Murray
2. b. Richard Attenborough
3. a. *It's a Wonderful Life*
4. c. *The World Is Not Enough*
5. c. *Jingle All the Way*
6. a. Michael Caine
7. b. *Jack Frost*
8. b. Peter Auty
9. a. Hulk Hogan
10. c. Tom Conti

House

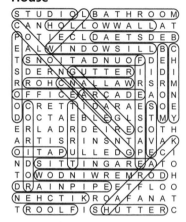

An attic ladder is a retractable ladder that is installed into the floor of an attic.

Themeless 1

B	O	S	C		F	R	O	S	H		S	A	F	E
O	T	T	O		R	O	U	T	E		O	R	R	A
S	T	A	N	L	A	U	R	E	L		A	M	E	S
S	E	R	V	I	C	E		A	M	E	N	I	T	Y
A	R	R	E	S	T		B	L	E	N	D	S		
			R	A	I	S	A			T	E	S	T	E	D
W	A	F	T		O	O	N	A		M	O	I	R	A
R	B	I		U	N	H	A	P	P	Y		C	I	I
E	R	R	O	R		O	N	E	R		M	E	N	S
N	A	S	C	A	R		A	D	O	B	E			
			T	E	N	E	T	S		M	A	L	L	E	T
R	O	B	L	O	W	E		O	P	E	R	A	T	E
A	R	O	O		A	P	O	S	T	R	O	P	H	E
P	E	R	T		R	E	N	A	L		S	E	E	N
S	S	N	S		D	E	A	R	Y		E	L	L	Y

Cards at the Table

Keep Going

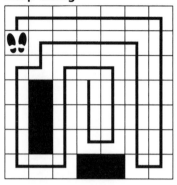

DELETE ONE • DELETE E AND FIND A FANTASY FILM.

Time

1. per diem—[A] daily. Your allowance is 75 cents *per diem*.

2. noctambulist—[B] sleepwalker. As a fridge-raiding *noctambulist*, I've wrecked my diet plan.

3. fortnight—[B] two weeks. The roofers will be back in a *fortnight* to add the gutters.

4. soiree—[C] evening party. By coincidence, six different guests brought baked beans to my *soiree*.

5. circadian—[C] in 24-hour cycles. We can't sleep—jet lag has skewed our *circadian* rhythms.

6. ides—[B] mid-month days. The *ides* of March were cold and wet, and the last day was no lamb.

7. adjourn—[C] call it a day. The committee was pooped and had to *adjourn* early.

8. curfew—[C] restriction at night. I can't go out—with the SAT approaching, my parents have imposed a 9 p.m. *curfew*.

9. reveille—[B] wake-up call. Buck's ringtone is a boot camp bugler's *reveille*.

10. crepuscular—[A] at twilight. On the front porch, I swing to the cicadas' *crepuscular* serenade.

11. repast—[C] time of a meal. Though I prefer to eat outside, on busy days, I take my midday *repast* at my desk.

12. contemporary—[C] present-day. "Egad!" and "zounds!" are not exactly *contemporary* expressions.

13. du jour—[A] just for today. The restaurant's soup *du jour* is French onion.

14. swing shift—[A] 4 p.m. to midnight. I feel out of whack after working the *swing shift*.

15. advent—[C] coming or arrival. With the *advent* of the holidays, we'll try to start our shopping early but will probably give in to our tradition of late gift giving!

VOCABULARY RATINGS
9 & below: Dawning light
10–12: Good day's work
13–15: Brightest star

PAGE 16
Sport Maze

ONE LETTER LESS OR MORE • NOTEPAD

PAGE 17
Tic-Tac-Toe Winners

PAGE 18
Top That

English muffin 6. Only muffin 6 has three different toppings: cheese-ham-olive. All the other muffins have two toppings.

LETTER LINE • SUBLIMINAL; ALUMNI, MUSLIN, IAMB, NIMBUS, SIMIAN

PAGE 19
Word Sudoku

UNCANNY TURN • ENTRANCE

PAGE 20
The Ex-Files

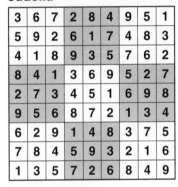

PAGE 21
Sudoku

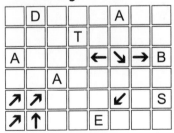

SYMBOL SUMS •
15 − 4 X 4 + 11 = 55

PAGE 22
Find the Right Word

DATABASE

CHANGELINGS • AQUAMARINE / CHARTREUSE / PERIWINKLE

PAGE 23

You Said It

G	R	A	B		K	A	T	I	E		B	A	G	S
R	O	M	A		I	V	A	N	A		E	L	I	E
E	B	O	N		L	O	U	T	S		E	A	R	L
Y	O	U	K	N	O	W	T	H	E	D	R	I	L	L
S	T	R	I	N	G			E	L	A	M			
			N	E	R	D	S		S	T	U	D	I	O
H	A	N	G		A	R	T	Y		E	G	Y	P	T
O	B	I		E	M	E	R	A	L	D		E	S	O
R	E	L	A	X		D	I	R	E		A	D	O	S
S	L	E	U	T	H		A	N	V	I	L			
			T	R	U	E			I	S	R	A	E	L
Y	O	U	H	A	D	M	E	A	T	H	E	L	L	O
A	L	T	O		D	E	R	M	A		A	G	E	S
N	E	E	R		L	E	G	I	T		D	A	N	E
K	O	P	S		E	R	O	D	E			Y	E	A	R

PAGE 24

Futoshiki

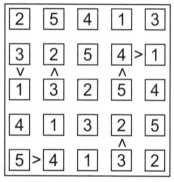

TRIANAGRAM • ELAPSE / PLEASE

PAGE 25

Famous Firsts

1. a. Germany, in 1885
2. a. Greece
3. b. The first person to reach the summit of Mount Everest
4. c. Cornflakes
5. a. Queen Victoria
6. a. New Zealand
7. a. Rugby—he was a student at Rugby School in England
8. b. Thomas Cook
9. a. "The Terrible"

PAGE 26

Letters

John. Per four letters if you switch the first two with the last two you get these four names: Vera, Bart, Nico and John.

QUICK CROSSWORD •

PAGE 27

Flirt

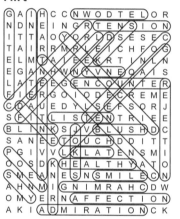

According to research, flirting is a good remedy for stress and it gives most men and women a kick.

PAGE 28

Pen Names

G	A	S	H		G	R	U	F	F		S	C	A	T
A	L	T	A		R	O	N	E	E		A	S	T	O
G	E	O	R	G	E	S	A	N	D		U	F	O	S
A	C	A	D	E	M	Y		S	E	A	S	O	N	S
			E	L	L			R	E	A	R			
E	L	A	S	T	I	C		L	A	R	G	E	S	S
V	E	N	T		N	A	T	A	L		E	S	T	O
I	N	N			T	I	C			T	A	D		
T	I	L	T		C	H	E	E	R		H	E	R	A
A	N	A	R	C	H	Y		D	E	P	A	R	T	S
		N	A	P	A			F	I	N				
R	A	D	I	A	N	T		D	R	E	D	G	E	S
A	T	E	N		C	U	R	R	E	R	B	E	L	L
M	O	R	E		E	L	I	A	S		A	N	K	A
A	P	S	E		S	L	O	T	H		G	A	S	P

PAGE 29

Spot the Differences

PAGE 30

Sudoku X

7	1	3	5	6	9	2	4	8
6	9	5	2	4	8	1	7	3
8	2	4	7	1	3	6	5	9
4	7	6	8	9	2	3	1	5
1	8	9	6	3	5	4	2	7
5	3	2	4	7	1	9	8	6
2	6	1	3	8	7	5	9	4
3	5	7	9	2	4	8	6	1
9	4	8	1	5	6	7	3	2

BLOCK ANAGRAM • SAND STORM

PAGE 31

Alliterative Guys

P	U	N	G		D	E	T	E	R		S	T	O	L
A	R	O	O		A	N	O	L	E		P	O	L	E
W	I	L	L	Y	W	O	N	K	A		O	M	E	N
N	A	T	I	O	N	S		E	S	K	I	M	O	S
S	H	E	A	R				O	I	L	Y			
			T	K	O	S		A	N	N	E	T	T	E
B	U	S	H		K	I	E	L		D	U	O	S	
R	N	A			S	E	R	V	E		N	O	T	
A	T	M	S			G	R	I	T		D	E	L	E
C	O	M	P	O	T	E		N	C	A	A			
	Y	O	R	E					S	Y	R	I	A	
I	N	S	T	E	A	D		S	K	A	T	I	N	G
L	O	O	T		P	E	T	E	R	P	I	P	E	R
E	R	S	E		O	B	E	L	I		M	E	R	E
A	M	A	D		T	I	N	A	S		E	N	T	E

203

PAGE 32

Medication

The combination of pills 1 and 4 because that finishes all possible two-pill combinations of the five available pills.

QUICK WORD SEARCH •

M U I L L A N E M O N E O A K
Z D I H C R O C U S O L I V E
H O S T A I L H A D Y N O E P
X O L H P F H S O M S O C Z P
C A L I L W O R R A Y L L O H

PAGE 33

Kakuro

1	8	9	■	3	9	1
2	1	5	■	5	6	2
8	■	2	9	8	7	6
■	2	4	7	■	3	■
7	4	■	2	1	■	■
2	1	■	8	6	1	7
9	3	1	■	4	2	8

SANDWICH • TAIL

PAGE 34

Title Role Players

D	I	S	C		T	E	A	C	H		S	M	E	E
A	S	H	E		H	Y	D	R	O		K	I	L	L
L	I	A	M	N	E	E	S	O	N		I	L	S	A
E	N	D	E	A	R	S		C	O	L	L	E	E	N
			N	R	A			R	O	L	Y			
C	U	R	T	A	I	L		R	E	B	E	C	C	A
O	T	O	S		N	O	S	E	D		T	Y	R	O
M	I	G				E	B	B			R	U	R	
I	C	E	T		A	W	E	E	K		M	U	S	T
C	A	R	R	E	R	E		C	A	L	I	S	T	A
	M	O	E	T			N	A	S					
P	R	O	T	E	I	N		E	S	T	H	E	R	S
L	O	O	T		S	A	L	M	A	H	A	Y	E	K
E	T	R	E		A	L	V	I	N		P	R	I	E
A	C	E	R		N	A	I	L	S		S	E	N	D

PAGE 35

Hourglass

(1) BRIGADE
(2) BADGER
(3) BREAD
(4) BARD
(5) BRAM
(6) AMBER
(7) MARBLE
(8) RAMBLER

PAGE 36

Sudoku Twin

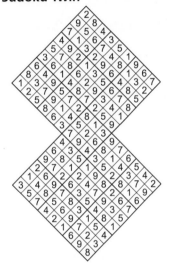

DELETE ONE • DELETE O AND FIND
A VALENTINE CARD

PAGE 37

Themeless 2

C	A	S	A		S	K	A	T	E		A	S	A	S
E	L	A	M		A	I	D	E	D		N	O	N	O
D	I	S	N	E	Y	L	A	N	D		I	M	A	N
E	C	H	E	L	O	N		S	I	A	M	E	S	E
S	E	A	S	O	N		S	E	E	S	A	W		
			T	I	A	R	A		D	I	T	H	E	R
A	R	M	Y		R	A	H	S		D	E	E	R	E
T	A	U		P	A	N	A	C	H	E		R	I	D
L	I	L	L	I		I	R	A	E		B	E	S	S
I	N	T	E	N	D		A	R	B	O	R			
			I	N	T	E	R	N		R	I	O	T	E	D
T	A	P	I	O	C	A		M	I	S	S	I	L	E
I	S	L	E		A	C	C	I	D	E	N	T	A	L
L	I	E	N		D	E	A	N	E		A	L	T	E
L	A	S	T		E	S	T	E	S		N	E	E	D

PAGE 38

Sport Maze

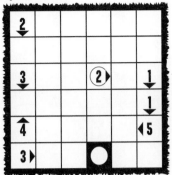

ONE LETTER LESS OR MORE •
NEGLECT

PAGE 39

Jack Nicholson

Jack Nicholson is called the best actor of his generation, together with Robert De Niro and Al Pacino.

Answers

Alliterative Gals

S	P	A	T		R	E	A	D	S		O	L	A	N
P	I	T	H		O	R	I	E	L		C	U	B	E
A	N	O	U	K	A	I	M	E	E		A	C	R	O
		R	I	S	K		M	E	G	R	Y	A	N	
K	I	S	M	E	T			V	E	I	L			
I	N	H	A	L	E	S		T	E	E	N	A	G	E
S	C	A	N		R	H	E	A	S		A	W	O	L
S	I	R			I	N	K				L	A	D	
E	T	O	N		O	P	T	E	D		P	E	L	E
D	E	N	I	E	R	S		N	E	M	E	S	I	S
	S	E	L	A			C	O	R	S	E	T		
O	U	T	L	I	N	E		S	L	O	T			
P	R	O	S		G	R	E	T	A	G	A	R	B	O
T	I	N	E		E	M	B	E	R		I	D	O	L
O	M	E	N		S	A	B	R	E		N	A	P	E

Number Cube

9. The combined total of the numbers is written under every cube.

DOODLE PUZZLE • RAILinG

Triangle Teaser

X = 27.
A (16 + 17 + 18) − (7 + 8 + 9) = 27
B (13 + 14 + 15) − (4 + 5 + 6) = 27
C (10 + 11 + 12) − (1 + 2 + 3) = 27

Word Sudoku

L	J	H	M	P	E	T	G	I
P	I	G	T	H	J	M	L	E
T	E	M	L	I	G	H	P	J
J	G	P	E	T	M	L	I	H
M	T	I	P	L	H	E	J	G
H	L	E	J	G	I	P	T	M
E	H	L	I	J	T	G	M	P
I	M	T	G	E	P	J	H	L
G	P	J	H	M	L	I	E	T

UNCANNY TURN • GRAND FINALE

Things To Be Thankful For

LETTERBLOCKS • CHIMNEY / SNOWMAN

Binairo

0	0	1	1	0	0	1	1	0	0	1	1
1	0	0	1	0	1	1	0	0	1	0	1
0	1	1	0	1	0	0	1	1	0	1	0
0	1	0	0	1	0	1	0	1	1	0	1
1	0	1	1	0	1	1	0	0	1	0	0
0	0	1	0	1	1	0	1	1	0	1	0
1	1	0	1	0	0	1	0	1	0	0	1
1	1	0	0	1	1	0	1	0	1	0	0
0	0	1	0	1	0	0	1	1	0	1	1
0	0	1	1	0	1	1	0	0	1	0	1
1	1	0	0	1	0	0	1	0	1	1	0
1	1	0	1	0	1	0	0	1	0	1	0

LETTERBLOCKS • CHIMNEY / SNOWMAN

Splish Splash

1. Johnny Weissmuller
2. Butterfly
3. Backstroke
4. 1,500 meters
5. Niagara Falls
6. The Bahamas
7. Elephants; they use their trunks as snorkels
8. Benjamin Franklin
9. Spit—approximately 25,000 quarts of it
10 Tortoise shell
11. The breaststroke
12. Over 10 minutes

Explorers

R	O	O	D		P	R	A	M		M	A	C	R	O
A	R	T	E		L	A	D	E		A	B	H	O	R
J	O	H	N	C	A	B	O	T		R	I	A	N	T
A	N	E	M	O	N	E			E	N	I	G	M	A	S
H	O	R	A	C	E			A	S	A	P			
			R	O	T	S		T	R	A	I	L	E	R
B	A	S	K		S	T	O	I	C		L	A	L	O
O	R	A			U	A	R				I	A	M	
S	E	L	F		S	P	R	E	E		E	N	N	A
C	A	L	I	S	T	A		D	A	H	S			
	Y	E	T	I			R	E	C	A	N	T		
C	O	R	N	E	R	S		C	A	R	A	B	O	O
O	V	I	N	E		M	A	R	C	O	P	O	L	O
S	E	D	E	R		U	T	A	H		E	V	A	N
T	R	E	S	S		G	A	M	E		D	E	N	S

Horoscope

DELETE ONE • DELETE E AND FIND **LEADING MAN**

LETTERBLOCKS • MONSTER / VAMPIRE

Sudoku

2	1	8	6	3	7	5	4	9
9	5	7	1	4	8	2	3	6
3	4	6	5	9	2	7	8	1
5	7	1	8	2	3	9	6	4
6	9	3	7	1	4	8	2	5
4	8	2	9	5	6	1	7	3
7	6	5	4	8	1	3	9	2
8	2	9	3	6	5	4	1	7
1	3	4	2	7	9	6	5	8

Answers

SYMBOL SUMS •
$2 \div 1 + 6 \times 6 = 48$

End to End

R	U	T	H		S	O	A	P	S		O	M	E	N
A	F	R	O		K	A	R	A	T		P	U	R	E
F	O	U	R	B	Y	F	O	U	R		A	C	N	E
		M	O	B	S		L	U	N	C	H	E	D	
S	C	H	O	O	L			D	O	I	T			
C	R	A	N	K	U	P		R	E	S	T	O	R	E
R	I	L	E		E	A	S	E	L		Y	O	U	R
I	M	F			Y	E	A				M	B	A	
M	E	A	D		R	E	E	L	S		H	U	B	S
P	A	N	A	C	H	E		M	O	N	O	C	L	E
		D	R	A	Y			N	E	T	H	E	R	
R	E	H	E	A	T	S		E	A	R	S			
E	T	A	S		H	E	A	D	T	O	H	E	A	D
M	O	L	T		M	E	D	I	A		O	R	C	A
I	N	F	O		S	P	O	T	S		T	R	E	Y

Read the Flags

Flag 3 is the only flag that hasn't been shown yet.

CHANGELINGS• CONTRIBUTE / SUPPORTIVE / BENEFICIAL

The Doctor Is In

1. Thing 1 and Thing 2
2. The fish
3. Two
4. Cindy-Lou
5. *Sam-I-Am*
6. *And To Think That I Saw It on Mulberry Street*
7. *The Sneetches and Other Stories*
8. *Yertle the Turtle*
9. *Horton*
10. *One Fish, Two Fish, Red Fish, Blue Fish*
11. Mount Crumpit
12. Kites

Number Cluster

DELETE ONE • DELETE O AND FIND **PHONETICALLY**

DOODLE PUZZLE • ComPOST

Tricky Triangles

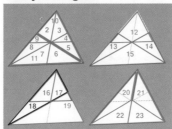

WORD WALL • COMPARTMENTALIZING / MISTRUSTFULNESS / ALLITERATION / ANTIPATHY / MISLED / DEN

Golden Globe Winners

A	N	S	E		I	N	L	A	W		G	E	A	R
D	O	W	N		M	O	I	R	A		U	R	S	A
A	L	E	G		M	O	N	A	D		A	N	T	I
G	I	L	L	I	A	N	A	N	D	E	R	S	O	N
E	N	L	I	S	T			L	L	D				
		S	T	U	N		L	E	V	E	L	E	D	
L	A	S	H		R	O	P	E		E	D	I	N	A
E	E	N		C	E	R	E	A	L	S		F	O	R
E	R	A	T	O		M	E	S	A		C	O	S	T
J	I	G	S	A	W	S		E	V	E	R			
		U	T	A				E	L	A	I	N	E	
J	E	N	N	I	F	E	R	A	N	I	S	T	O	N
U	V	E	A		F	R	O	N	D		H	A	R	D
D	E	E	M		L	A	T	T	E		E	L	S	E
I	N	R	I		E	T	H	E	R		D	Y	E	D

Name the Sport

P	A	W	S		C	R	E	D	O		A	W	L	S
A	T	E	E		R	I	V	E	R		B	A	I	O
V	O	L	L	E	Y	B	A	L	L		S	T	A	B
E	N	D	L	E	S	S		L	E	T	T	E	R	S
D	E	S	E	R	T			A	D	A	R			
		R	O	A	M		I	N	S	I	P	I	D	
C	A	W	S		L	A	U	D	S		N	O	D	E
H	E	R			R	A	E				L	O	S	
A	R	E	A		L	I	L	A	C		P	O	L	K
D	I	S	D	A	I	N		L	A	S	H			
		T	U	N	E			N	E	I	G	H	S	
W	I	L	L	I	A	M		S	C	A	L	L	O	P
E	L	I	A		B	A	S	K	E	T	B	A	L	L
A	I	N	T		E	M	A	I	L		I	D	E	A
R	A	G	E		D	E	N	T	S		N	E	S	T

Keeping Score

6. The difference in the scores forms the following series: − 2, + 4, − 6, + 8. Alternating per column you also see the following two series: 7-14-21-28 and 9-18-27-36.

CLOCKWISE • MATHEMATICAL
1. MALLARD
2. ACCUSED
3. THYROID
4. HATCHED
5. ESCAPED
6. MANGLED
7. ALARMED
8. TOASTED
9. INHALED
10. CHECKED
11. ASSURED
12. LATCHED

Answers

PAGE 58

Frankenstein

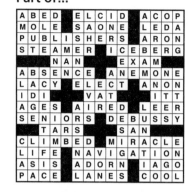

Frankenstein is the name of the doctor that created the monster, not the monster itself.

PAGE 59

Futoshiki

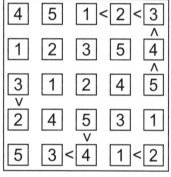

TRIANAGRAM • HEIGHTS / HIGHEST

PAGE 60

Part of...

PAGE 61

Keep Going

DELETE ONE • DELETE H AND FIND **PRACTICAL JOKE**

PAGE 62

Hear, Here!

1. gambol—[A] frolic (sounds like: gamble). After Dorothy's house killed the Wicked Witch, the Munchkins *gamboled* and sang.

2. humerus—[A] arm bone (sounds like: humorous). To find your *humerus*, look between your shoulder and elbow.

3. discrete—[C] separate (sounds like: discreet). The king's men found Humpty Dumpty in a thousand *discrete* pieces.

4. carrel—[A] study alcove (sounds like: carol). I'll be cramming in a library *carrel*.

5. appellation—[B] name or title (sounds like: Appalachian). Ted prefers the *appellation* Sir Hugh Highcastle.

6. pore—[A] read attentively (sounds like: pour and poor). Jack Sparrow *pored* over the soggy treasure map.

7. dissent—[C] difference of opinion (sounds like: descent). Between Zoë and her mom, there is some *dissent* regarding bedtime.

8. straiten—[B] hem in (sounds like: straighten). Rodney was *straitened* by the cliff behind him and the lions in front of him.

9. martial—[B] relating to war (sounds like: marshal). We enjoy clapping to *martial* music on the Fourth of July.

10. gild—[B] cover with a thin layer of gold (sounds like: guild). The artist carefully *gilded* the mirror's ornate wood frame.

11. complementary—[C] having mutually completing parts (sounds like: complimentary). Count Dracula was wearing a tasteful black suit with a *complementary* cape.

12. signet—[B] seal (sounds like: cygnet). The deal isn't official until the queen stamps her *signet* on it.

13. principle—[B] rule or doctrine (sounds like: principal). As a *principle*, Dr. Frankenstein keeps spare parts in case his monster needs a tune-up.

14. pallet—[B] bed (sounds like: palette). The weary traveler gratefully slept on the straw-filled *pallet*.

15. augur—[C] reader of omens (sounds like: auger). Due to the home team's inexperience, I don't need an *augur* to predict this game will be a blowout.

VOCABULARY RATINGS
9 & below: Sonically challenged
10–12: Good listener
13–15: Sound thinker

PAGE 63

Sport Maze

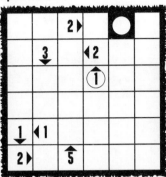

ONE LETTER LESS OR MORE • NEITHER

PAGE 64

A Number of Films

B	E	N	S		W	A	L	K	S		R	A	S	P
A	L	I	E		A	G	E	N	T		A	R	I	E
B	A	N	C		T	H	R	E	E	K	I	N	G	S
A	M	E	R	I	C	A		E	V	I	D	E	N	T
	T	E	S	H			E	N	E					
C	L	O	T	H	E	S		E	N	G	R	O	S	S
R	E	F	S		D	A	R	N	S		S	N	I	T
E	P	I			R	E	D				E	L	A	
W	E	V	E		H	A	V	O	C		A	F	A	R
S	W	E	N	S	O	N		R	E	A	L	I	S	T
	Q	U	M			R	O	A	N					
S	E	C	U	R	E	D		H	E	L	M	E	T	S
T	W	O	I	F	B	Y	S	E	A		O	D	I	E
L	E	A	R		O	N	E	A	L		D	A	N	E
O	R	L	E		Y	E	L	L	S		E	Y	E	S

PAGE 65

Peak Puzzle

Number 8. The combined total of the four numbers on the three sides of the imaginary triangle always equals 100. The combined total of the numbers of the same color always equals 75.

BLOCK ANAGRAM • INDIAN SUMMER

PAGE 66

Word Sudoku

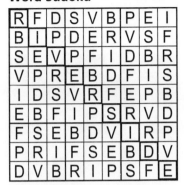

THREE-IN-ONE • ZAMBEZI / YANGTZE / GANGES

PAGE 67

Fine Furniture

1. Armoire
2. London
3. Queen Anne
4. Bureau
5. Veneer
6. In times of war, the silver mountings were melted down and turned into silver coins
7. Bauhaus
8. Mother of pearl
9. The United States.
10. A sideboard
11. Pedastal table
12. The style, the maker, or even a patent granted to the company.

PAGE 68

Cage the Animals

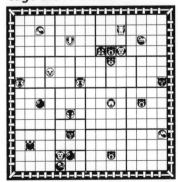

FRIENDS • EACH CAN HAVE THE PREFIX **CON-** TO FORM A NEW WORD.

PAGE 69

'60s Slang

S	T	O	A		B	E	S	O	M		I	B	I	S
T	O	T	S		A	P	A	C	E		N	U	D	E
O	U	T	T	A	S	I	G	H	T		S	M	E	E
A	C	E	R	B	I	C		R	E	S	U	M	E	D
T	H	R	I	L	L		P	E	O	P	L	E		
		D	E	I	C	E		R	E	A	D	E	R	
A	S	H	E		C	O	D	A		C	R	O	C	E
B	O	A		C	A	N	A	R	D	S		U	T	E
B	O	N	G	O		S	N	E	E		S	T	O	L
A	N	G	O	R	A		T	O	P	I	C			
		L	O	A	V	E	S		A	N	I	M	A	L
D	O	O	D	L	E	R		O	R	D	E	R	L	Y
A	T	O	M		R	I	G	H	T	O	N	M	A	N
R	O	S	A		S	C	A	R	E		C	O	R	D
K	E	E	N		E	A	S	E	D		E	M	M	A

PAGE 70

Binairo

I	I	O	O	I	O	I	I	O	I	O
O	I	I	O	I	O	I	I	O	I	O
I	O	I	I	O	I	O	I	O	O	I
I	O	O	I	O	O	I	I	O	I	I
O	I	I	O	I	I	O	I	I	O	O
I	I	O	I	I	O	I	O	I	O	O
O	O	I	I	O	I	I	O	O	I	I
O	O	I	O	I	I	O	I	I	O	I
I	I	O	I	O	O	I	O	I	I	O
O	O	I	O	I	I	O	I	O	I	I
I	I	O	I	O	I	O	O	I	O	I

LETTERBLOCKS • FANTASY / FICTION

PAGE 71

Sweet Treat

Plate 6. There is an equal number of cookies of the same color on each plate. Plate six is the only plate that has 0 cookies of the same color.

QUICK WORD SEARCH •

G	O	L	D	S	T	O	N	E	T	I	T	K	E	T
S	P	H	E	N	E	P	H	R	I	T	E	D	A	J
Z	A	A	M	E	T	H	Y	S	T	E	N	R	A	G
I	L	N	A	I	D	I	S	B	O	L	Y	R	E	B
M	O	O	N	S	T	O	N	E	T	I	L	L	E	M

Answers

PAGE 72
'70s Slang

(crossword grid)

PAGE 73
Nursing

(word search grid)

The motivation of the men and women who work in nursing is mainly to help and assist people.

PAGE 74
Word Wheel

per, pie, pro, rip, pier, poor, prof, ripe, rope, prier, prior, proof, repro, roper, proffer, reproof, fireproof.

SANDWICH • TRAIN

PAGE 75
Queens

(crossword grid)

PAGE 76
Sudoku

7	8	5	6	9	3	4	2	1
2	1	9	4	7	5	8	3	6
6	3	4	8	2	1	9	7	5
9	5	1	3	4	6	7	8	2
3	2	8	9	5	7	6	1	4
4	7	6	2	1	8	5	9	3
1	6	7	5	3	9	2	4	8
5	9	2	1	8	4	3	6	7
8	4	3	7	6	2	1	5	9

SYMBOL SUMS •
$24 + 25 - 1 \div 8 = 6$

PAGE 77
Whorls

C. It spirals anticlockwise. The other figures all spiral clockwise.

PAGE 78
Themeless 3

(crossword grid)

PAGE 79
Alphablock

O. Read the vertical list as a series of three letters further in the alphabet. Read the horizontal list as a series of four letters back in the alphabet.

DOODLE PUZZLE • GRandFATher

PAGE 80
Kings

(crossword grid)

PAGE 81

Do the Math

9	−	8	×	7	=	7
÷		+		×		
3	+	4	÷	1	=	7
×		−		−		
6	−	5	+	2	=	3
=		=		=		
18		7		5		

DOUBLETALK • COAL/KOHL

PAGE 82

Word Pyramid

(1) BE
(2) BED
(3) DEBT
(4) DEBUT
(5) BUSTED
(6) DUMBEST
(7) STUMBLED

PAGE 83

Sudoku

6	1	9	4	7	3	5	8	2
2	7	5	9	6	8	3	1	4
4	8	3	1	2	5	7	6	9
3	5	4	7	1	9	6	2	8
8	2	6	3	5	4	1	9	7
7	9	1	2	8	6	4	3	5
5	3	2	6	9	7	8	4	1
1	4	7	8	3	2	9	5	6
9	6	8	5	4	1	2	7	3

SYMBOL SUMS •
$3 \times 56 − 3 ÷ 3 = 55$

PAGE 84

Atomic Numbers

PAGE 85

Futoshiki

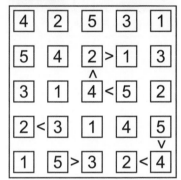

TRIANAGRAM • STRAP / TRAPS

PAGE 86

Corrections

7 and 5. Each set in the series consists of one digit more and the combined total of these digits equals 9.

WORD WALL • SEMIRESPECTABILITY / PERMISSIBLENESS / TERRIFICALLY, RACETRACK / ENROLL / WRY

PAGE 87

Famous Firsts

PAGE 88

Classical Capers

1. d. Mozart
2. a. From the New World
3. b. J. S. Bach
4. c. Rigoletto
5. a. Billy Budd
6. a. Edvard Grieg
7. c. Fidelio
8. a. Johann Strauss
9. a. Air on a G String
10. c. Slow the music

PAGE 89

Jurisprudence

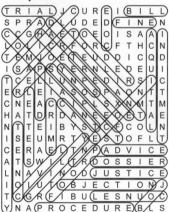

Jurisprudence is all of the judicial decisions made by courts of law and tribunals.

PAGE 90
Sport Maze

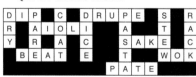

ONE LETTER LESS OR MORE • NERVOUS

PAGE 93
Sudoku X

8	1	3	5	4	6	2	9	7
5	7	2	9	8	1	6	4	3
9	4	6	7	2	3	5	1	8
4	8	7	1	5	2	3	6	9
6	2	1	8	3	9	7	5	4
3	5	9	6	7	4	1	8	2
2	3	8	4	1	5	9	7	6
7	9	5	3	6	8	4	2	1
1	6	4	2	9	7	8	3	5

BLOCK ANAGRAM • WEATHER FRONT

PAGE 96
Do the Math

8	-	5	+	3	=	6
-		+		-		
6	+	9	-	1	=	14
+		-		+		
7	-	4	+	2	=	5
=		=		=		
9		10		4		

DOUBLETALK • AUGER/AUGUR

PAGE 91
Their Final Films 1

```
E E L S   S T I L T   I C E T
T R O I   O W N E R   T A X I
H E N R Y F O N D A   A R I D
O C E L O T S   A C O L Y T E
S T R O D E     T R I G
    I A N S   R O B A R D S
B A R N   S W E A R   N A R A
O N A   A R I     N U T
O N U S   A R E N A   A T M S
M A L C O L M   S P A T
  J A I L     P I L O T S
T H U N D E R   P A N A C H E
H E L D   R O B E R T S H A W
A R I A   G U I S E   E R N E
D E A L   Y E N T L   S E E D
```

PAGE 94
Their Final Films 2

```
D A T A   M A R I N   M A S T
E L A N   A D E L E   A N N O
B E T T E D A V I S   G N A R
T R E L L I S   A T T E M P T
S T R E S S     L O N I
    R E O S   K E T T L E S
P A L S   N A I A D   A L T E
O R I     L O B     E N A
O O Z E   S E N O R   C R A M
H O T L I P S   B A R A
    A E R O   D I S M A L
P A Y M E N T   S I N C E R E
O R L E   G R E T A G A R B O
E L O N   E A S E L   D I O N
M O R T   S P O T S   E T R E
```

PAGE 97
Long-Running Musicals

```
W I S P   R O A M S   S P A M
E S P Y   A L L A H   W A C O
L A I R   L E O N A   E U R O
L A C A G E A U X F O L L E S
S C A M P I     F A T A
    I A G O   D E F E C T S
A B C D   H O M E R   R O R Y
L O O     Z A G     L O N
D O N T   R E G A N   F E T E
A N D R O I D   S O U L
    E A R N     B R O O M S
A N N I E G E T Y O U R G U N
C U S P   I V I E D   I L S A
I D E S   N I N N Y   D E E P
D E D E   G L A S S   A D D S
```

PAGE 92
Kakuro

8	5	1		4	8	3	9	6
9	7	2		1	9		8	4
	4	3	8	2		3	2	1
1	2		7	5	1	9	3	
8	9	6	2		3	7	6	9
3		8	9	2	6		1	2
6	8	9		1	8	9		1
9	2				9	3	8	7
5	1	2	3		4	9	8	

SANDWICH • GREEN

PAGE 95
Under Your Skin

Skin cell 3. The colors are repeated in each column and the nucleuses switch from black to white.

QUICK CROSSWORD •

```
D I P   C   D R U P E   S   R
R   A I O L I   A   T   A
Y   R   A   C   S A K E   C
B E A T E   E   T   W O K
        P A T E
```

PAGE 98
Letter Soup

Anchor, Yacht, Compass, Catamaran, Water, Regatta, Boom, Afterdeck

PAGE 99

Sudoku Twin

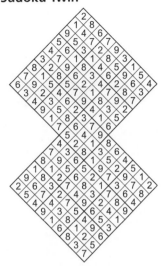

DELETE ONE • DELETE O AND FIND **ITALIAN OPERA**

PAGE 100

Secret Garden

S	P	C	A		D	E	N	E	B		A	P	O	D
A	R	A	B		E	N	A	T	E		P	R	E	Y
L	I	P	S		M	O	V	E	R		O	O	N	A
M	O	R	O	S	E	L	Y		N	E	L	S	O	N
A	R	A	R	A	T			I	D	L	E			
			B	L	E	W		R	E	S	O	L	V	E
C	A	P	E		R	O	S	E	S			Y	E	S
L	A	R	D			R	E	N			S	T	E	P
O	R	O			O	R	I	E	L		A	E	R	O
D	E	S	T	I	N	Y		W	E	A	R			
			E	R	I	E			A	B	A	C	U	S
N	I	C	E	S	T		K	E	R	O	S	E	N	E
A	R	U	M		I	N	U	R	N		O	R	C	A
V	E	T	O		M	O	R	S	E		T	E	A	R
I	S	E	R		E	N	T	E	R		A	S	P	S

PAGE 101

Christmas Lights

Christmas tree 2. On all the other Christmas trees the left and right sides are decorated with identically colored Christmas tree lights.

CLOCKWISE • CLIFFEHANGERS

1. CALUMNY
2. LITURGY
3. INFANCY
4. FACULTY
5. FALLACY
6. HARMONY
7. ALCHEMY
8. NOSEGAY
9. GRAVITY
10. ECSTASY
11. RECTIFY
12. SKETCHY

PAGE 102

Hourglass

(1) THERMOS
(1) MONSTER
(2) MENTOR
(3) METRO
(4) MORE
(5) EMIR
(6) CRIME
(7) METRIC
(8) THERMIC

PAGE 103

Machines

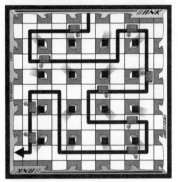

A machine is usually a type of electronic instrument used to perform a specific task.

PAGE 104

Beat the Heat

A	L	A	I		A	S	A	P		A	P	E
B	O	S	C		N	A	S	A		M	I	A
S	A	K	E		S	W	I	M	M	I	N	G
			B	E	E	S		P	A	S	T	E
S	C	R	A	W	L		S	E	N	S	O	R
I	R	A	T	E		A	I	R				
M	Y	T	H		F	A	N		P	I	U	S
			T	E	A		D	A	N	T	E	
A	D	H	E	R	E		C	O	R	N	E	T
T	R	U	C	E		O	R	C	A			
L	E	M	O	N	A	D	E		S	A	G	E
A	S	A		C	R	O	P		O	G	R	E
S	S	N		H	E	R	E		L	E	E	K

PAGE 105

Surveillance!

FRIENDS • THEY ARE ALL ENGLISH WORDS TAKEN FROM HINDI.

PAGE 106

Word Parts

SCROLLING, CABRIOLET, RADIATION, DANGEROUS, QUARTERLY, KNOCKDOWN

SANDWICH • OUT

PAGE 107

One Way

L	I	F	E		A	B	U	T		W	E	N	T
A	B	R	I		P	L	A	T	O		I	L	E	A
S	E	A	S		S	P	R	A	Y		G	O	A	L
T	A	M	A	L	E		S	H	O	W	G	I	R	L
	M	E	D	I	U	M		S	T	O	L		
		E	A	D	E	N		A	K	I	M	B	O
S	K	Y		R	O	N	D	O	S		N	O	E	L
L	O	A	N	S		U	S	S		O	G	L	E	D
A	B	R	A		A	S	T	H	M	A		E	T	S
M	E	N	T	A	L		R	E	E	T	H		
	U	M	B	O		A	D	E	L	I	E		
U	N	F	R	E	E	Z	E		A	R	M	A	D	A
P	A	R	A		R	A	V	E	L		E	M	I	T
O	V	A	L		T	W	I	N	S		N	O	L	O
N	E	T	S		S	A	L	E			C	K	E	N

PAGE 108

Lost in Translation

1. a. New Scotland
2. c. Lion Mountains
3. b. Puerto Rico
4. d. Nicaragua
5. a. Malta
6. b. Austria
7. d. Dominica
8. b. Sri Lanka
9. a. Taiwan
10. d. House of stone

PAGE 109

Impossible Path

Color 3. Look at the drawing like a folded ribbon that has three depth layers: purple (1) in the front, blue (2) in the middle, and green (3) at the rear.

LETTER LINE • MAINSTREAM; MARINATE, ARMAMENT, MISER, STAMMER, SIMMER

PAGE 110

Word Sudoku

H	C	B	M	E	R	D	I	A
A	E	I	D	H	B	R	C	M
D	M	R	C	A	I	E	B	H
I	H	M	B	R	A	C	E	D
C	R	D	E	I	M	A	H	B
B	A	E	H	D	C	M	R	I
E	D	A	R	B	H	I	M	C
M	I	H	A	C	E	B	D	R
R	B	C	I	M	D	H	A	E

THREE-IN-ONE • AMERICAN CIVIL, BOER, COLD

PAGE 111

A Tribal Gathering

1. d. Brazil
2. c. New Zealand
3. a. Africa
4. b. Survival
5. c. Niger Delta
6. a. Kenya
7. c. Sahara Desert
8. b. Central Africa
9. a. Angola
10. b. Ethiopia

PAGES 112-113

Weights

PAGE 114

Themeless 4

N	I	D	E		I	M	A	G	E		T	R	O	T
E	R	I	N		C	A	R	O	M		R	E	D	O
W	E	A	T	H	E	R	M	A	P		A	B	O	Y
E	N	N	E	A	D	S		D	O	D	G	E	R	S
L	E	A	R	N	T			R	A	I	L			
		I	D	E	A		C	I	R	C	L	E	S	
A	N	O	N		A	L	P	H	A		I	D	A	
B	O	R	G		L	A	E		D	O	G	G		
B	U	N		S	A	C	R	A		E	N	Y	A	
A	N	A	R	C	H	Y		I	S	M	S			
	M	E	S	A			P	A	T	R	O	L		
E	L	E	C	T	R	A		T	E	R	R	A	C	E
L	O	N	I		P	R	O	S	C	I	U	T	T	O
B	A	T	T		E	C	L	A	T		C	H	E	N
A	N	S	E		R	O	A	R	S		T	E	T	E

PAGE 115

Personality

1. craven—[C] cowardly. How *craven* to dump your beau via a text message!

2. picaresque—[A] like a daring rascal. Dashiell thinks wearing a cape makes him look more *picaresque*.

3. recluse—[B] hermit. You've never heard of Lady Gaga? You must be a *recluse*.

4. narcissist—[B] self-absorbed sort. What a *narcissist*, telling me every boring detail of his day!

5. ingratiate—[C] try to gain favor. To *ingratiate* herself with the pageant judges, Carla kept winking at them.

6. acolyte—[A] follower. No, I'm not with the band. I'm just one of the *acolytes*.

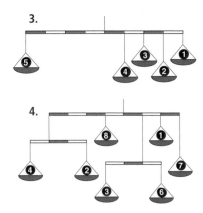

7. **bon vivant**—[C] lover of fine dining. If you need me, I'll be at the wine tasting with the other *bon vivants*.

8. **sanguine**—[A] optimistic. After a month of lessons, I feel *sanguine* about passing the road test.

9. **choleric**—[C] hot-tempered. The *choleric* judge pounded his gavel so hard that it broke.

10. **congenial**—[C] friendly. The catcher and the umpire seem too *congenial* to me.

11. **bloviate**—[B] rant pompously. To host a talk-radio show, it helps if you can b*loviate* on command.

12. **venal**—[B] corruptible. It's clear from the parade fiasco that your town supervisors are a bunch of *venal* crooks.

13. **bumptious**—[A] pushy. Becca only joined the choir because her *bumptious* mom nagged her into it.

14. **altruistic**—[B] kind to others. Piranhas are never described as *altruistic*.

15. **bohemian**—[B] nonconformist. Lulu's *bohemian* friends introduced her to edgy performance art.

VOCABULARY RATINGS
9 & below: Icebreaker
10–12: Good mixer
13–15: Life of the party

PAGE 116

Sudoku

2	5	3	4	7	1	6	9	8
9	8	7	3	6	2	4	5	1
6	1	4	8	5	9	3	7	2
7	4	5	2	8	6	1	3	9
3	6	8	1	9	7	5	2	4
1	2	9	5	3	4	8	6	7
5	3	2	9	1	8	7	4	6
4	7	1	6	2	3	9	8	5
8	9	6	7	4	5	2	1	3

SYMBOL SUMS •
11 X 3 − 13 ÷ 5 = 4

PAGE 117

Word Ladders
road, word, draw, drag, gran, gang
bank, bark, rank, earn, rent, note

PAGE 118

Futoshiki

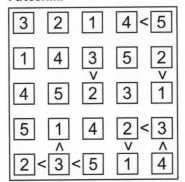

TRIANAGRAM • RICTUS / RUSTIC

PAGE 119

Not Related

S	A	G	S		P	A	R	I	S		M	A	C	E
H	U	R	T		R	H	E	T	T		A	L	A	W
A	R	O	E		O	S	I	E	R		C	I	R	E
F	A	I	R	Y	G	O	D	M	O	T	H	E	R	S
T	E	N	N	E	R			K	E	E	N			
			U	S	A	F		S	E	X	T	A	N	T
T	E	E	M		M	A	R	E	S		E	T	U	I
A	L	L				T	A	R			E	L	M	
L	I	E	F		N	A	H	U	M		I	D	L	E
C	A	P	I	T	O	L		M	O	O	N			
		H	E	A	R			D	E	C	I	D	E	
G	R	A	N	D	F	A	T	H	E	R	E	D	I	N
W	I	N	N		O	C	H	E	R		N	O	V	A
E	T	T	E		L	E	A	R	N		S	L	O	T
N	E	S	S		K	R	I	S	S		E	S	T	E

PAGE 120

Long Road Home
1. Battle Hymn of the Republic
2. Road
3. Arizona, New Mexico and Oklahoma
4. Henry Fonda
5. Jane Darwell
6. John Ford
7. All makeup and perfume
8. To pick fruit in California
9. Gum

PAGE 121

Building Blocks
47 blocks

DOODLE PUZZLE • HandBag

PAGE 122

Picasso

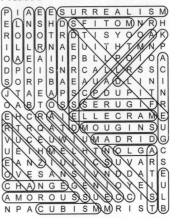

In his youth, Pablo Picasso painted up to three canvases a day in Paris.

PAGE 123

Three Amigos

B	A	L	T		A	T	I	L	T		M	I	C	A
I	T	A	S		N	A	D	I	A		A	R	A	L
F	R	I	E	N	D	P	A	L	C	O	H	O	R	T
F	A	C	T	O	R	S		T	O	R	O	N	T	O
			S	R	O			M	A	G				
A	R	T	E	M	I	S		M	A	T	A	D	O	R
S	E	A		A	D	A	N	O		E	N	U	R	E
A	T	M	S		S	P	E	N	T		Y	A	R	N
B	R	I	A	N		I	D	A	H	O		N	I	T
C	O	L	L	A	R	D		D	E	P	R	E	S	S
			E	N	E			O	T	A				
A	W	E	S	O	M	E		O	R	I	N	O	C	O
C	H	U	M	S	I	D	E	K	I	C	K	B	U	D
T	I	L	E		S	N	A	R	E		E	I	R	E
S	P	A	N		S	A	R	A	S		D	E	L	A

213

PAGE 124

Spot the Differences

PAGE 125

Word Wheel

ice, sec, sic, tic, cent, cite, nice, sect, scent, since, incise, incite, insect, nicest, iciness, scientist.

SANDWICH • CAP

PAGE 126

That's Life

A	B	A	T	E		A	P	P	A	L		R	E	F
R	E	D	U	X		G	A	R	B	O		E	R	A
A	L	I	T	T	L	E	W	O	R	K		D	R	U
T	A	T	T	O	O	S		C	A	I	S	S	O	N
		U	R	L		P	O	D		E	E	L	S	
A	L	I	T	T	L	E	S	L	E	E	P	A		
N	O	R		Y	A	Y		D	E	A				
G	U	A	V	A		R	C	A		K	L	E	I	N
		O	P	S		H	I	C			P	O	E	
	L	I	T	T	L	E	L	O	V	E	A	N	D	
O	R	A	L		A	I	D		B	I	N			
S	U	M	A	T	R	A		G	O	O	D	I	N	G
A	R	B		I	T	I	S	A	L	L	O	V	E	R
G	A	D		M	U	S	E	R		E	R	O	S	E
E	L	A		S	P	E	N	D		T	A	R	T	Y

PAGE 127

Towering

Tower 7

WORD WALL •
THERMOELECTROMETER /
SENSATIONALISTS / DERMABRASION,
ITINERANT / NAUSEA / ICE

PAGE 128

The Puzzled Librarian

1. *The Yellow Birds*
2. *The Middlesteins*
3. *Sweet Tooth*
4. *The Power of Habit*
5. *Consider the Fork*
6. *The Cove*
7. *Prague Fatale*
8. *Above All Things*
9. *Dear Life*
10. *A Week in Winter*

SANDWICH • WALK

PAGE 129

2012 Hits

A	H	A	B		S	C	A	L	P		E	W	E	S
L	O	C	O		C	A	R	O	L		D	I	V	E
D	R	U	N	K	O	N	Y	O	U		I	D	E	A
E	S	T	E	L	L	E		P	R	O	T	E	S	T
N	E	E	D	E	D			A	R	I	A			
			R	E	E	S		E	L	B	O	W	E	D
R	U	B	Y		D	A	V	I	S		N	A	T	O
I	S	O		J	A	G				K	O	N		
P	A	Y	S		O	A	T	H	S		R	E	N	T
A	F	F	L	E	C	K		T	U	B	E			
		R	A	N	T			N	E	B	U	L	A	
C	R	I	M	S	O	N		T	R	E	A	T	E	D
A	H	E	M		B	A	C	K	I	N	T	I	M	E
R	E	N	E		E	T	H	O	S		E	L	U	L
L	A	D	D		R	E	E	S	E		S	E	R	E

PAGE 130

Symbolic Science

1. **a.** Argon
2. **c.** Bromine
3. **c.** Calcium
4. **b.** Cobalt
5. **a.** Sulphur
6. **b.** Silver
7. **a.** Platinum
8. **c.** Nickel
9. **a.** Rhodium
10. **b.** Lead

PAGE 131

Hourglass

(1) PREDICT
(2) CREDIT
(3) TIRED
(4) EDIT
(5) DATE
(6) TRADE
(7) THREAD
(8) HYDRATE

PAGE 132

Maze

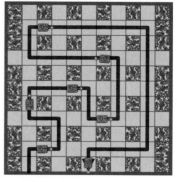

THREE-IN-ONE • TACAMA / GOBI / CHIHUAHUAN

PAGE 133

Non-Violence

A	R	O	D		O	P	E	R	A		A	C	T
R	A	N	I		R	O	M	A	N	A		B	A	A
I	N	E	V	E	R	L	I	K	E	D	G	U	N	S
A	D	I	E	U		I	T	E		D	O	S	E	S
			S	R	A	S			T	O	L	E	D	O
I	H	A	T	E	T	H	E	M	A	N	D			
J	E	T	S	K	I		N	O	R		A	M	I	D
K	R	A		A	N	T	O	I	N	E		A	C	E
L	A	P	P		G	A	L		I	D	A	H	O	S
			I	A	L	W	A	Y	S	B	L	I	N	K
S	C	R	A	P	E		C	H	E	T				
A	L	I	N	E		E	S	L		R	O	B	I	E
B	E	F	O	R	E	T	H	E	Y	G	O	O	F	F
L	O	L		S	E	R	A	P	E		N	E	A	T
E	N	E		K	E	N	T	S		A	R	T	S	

PAGE 134

Hotel Transylvania

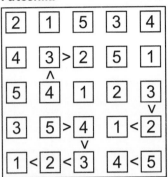

PAGE 135

Sport Maze

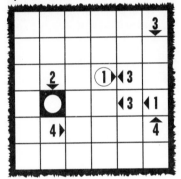

ONE LETTER LESS OR MORE •
MAGNETRON

PAGE 136

Directions

After sign T you are back at
intersection A.

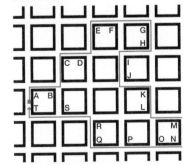

BLOCK ANAGRAM •
THUNDERSTORM

PAGE 137

Kitchen Utensils

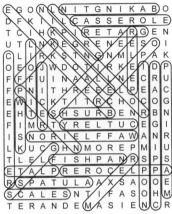

Good kitchen utensils make work
in the kitchen much more pleasant,
faster and easier.

PAGE 138

Word Sudoku

UNCANNY TURN • DISCREET

PAGE 139

Futoshiki

TRIANAGRAM • CRATER / CARTER

PAGE 140

Themeless 5

PAGE 141

Horoscope

DELETE ONE • DELETE A AND FIND
MERMAID.

LETTERBLOCKS • BUZZARD /
FEATHER

PAGE 142

Deuce

M. Replace all letters with the number of their place in the alphabet. Between the letters A-E-M-P is the letter that has the value of the number of letters that are skipped. Three (C) letters are skipped between A and E.

FRIENDS • EACH CAN HAVE THE SUFFIX -LET TO FORM A NEW WORD.

PAGE 143

Love at the Movies

PAGE 144

Geek Squad

PAGE 145

Sudoku

7	6	1	2	9	5	4	3	8
8	3	4	6	1	7	9	2	5
2	5	9	4	3	8	6	1	7
5	2	7	1	8	9	3	4	6
9	4	8	3	6	2	7	5	1
6	1	3	7	5	4	2	8	9
4	8	5	9	2	6	1	7	3
1	9	2	5	7	3	8	6	4
3	7	6	8	4	1	5	9	2

LETTERBLOCKS • GLITTER / PARTIES

PAGE 146

Number Cluster

7	5	3	3	3
7	8	5	5	5	5
7	8	8	6	4	4
7	1	8	6	4	2
7	7	8	6	4	2
8	8	8	6	6	6

DELETE ONE • DELETE S AND FIND DEPARTURE LOUNGE.

DOODLE PUZZLE • ViCar

PAGE 147

Opposite Number

PAGES 148

Number Targets

1. **X = 20.** Start at the top right-hand corner and work along the top line, then back along the second line, and so on. The numbers progress as follows: +3, -2, +1. Finish at the bottom left-hand corner square with 20.

2. The top number on each target is formed by multiplying the numbers in the previous set. The bottom number on each target is formed by adding together the previous two numbers.

   330
   41

3. **X = 48.** Working down the first target, multiply by 3 and add 1 each time. Going down target 2, multiply by 3 and add 2 each time, and going down target 3, multiply by 3 and add 3 each time.

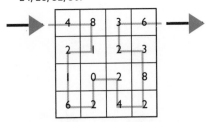

PAGES 149

Amazing Number Maze

Follow the route shown below to unravel the sequence 4, 8, 12, 16, 20, 24, 28, 32, 36.

PAGE 150

One Way

WORD WALL •
DISENFRANCHISEMENT / TEMPESTUOUSNESS / PERFIDIOUSLY / SONNETEER / ELITES./ PER

PAGE 151

Sound

Sound moves in waves that are caught by the auricle and carried inside.

PAGE 152

Film Quotes 1

PAGE 153

Fencing

Posts 4, 3 and 5. A large and a small post always alternate. The large posts alternate between black and white so B = 3. The small posts follow the color pattern gray, black and white combined with the shape pattern pointed and round.

CLOCKWISE • MONOSYLLABLE

1. MASKING
2. ONGOING
3. NAGGING
4. OPENING
5. SAPLING
6. YAWNING
7. LASTING
8. LACKING
9. AMBLING
10. BOOTLEG
11. LOLLING
12. EVOKING

PAGE 154

Sudoku X

6	9	5	4	3	2	8	1	7
8	4	7	5	1	9	3	2	6
2	3	1	6	7	8	9	5	4
5	2	9	3	4	6	7	8	1
1	7	3	9	8	5	6	4	2
4	8	6	1	2	7	5	3	9
9	1	4	7	5	3	2	6	8
7	5	8	2	6	1	4	9	3
3	6	2	8	9	4	1	7	5

BLOCK ANAGRAM •
ANTICYCLONE

PAGE 155

Novel Ideas

1. **a.** *The Fisher King*
2. **c.** C. S. Lewis
3. **c.** Umberto Eco
4. **a.** Mario Puzo
5. **a.** *The Dam Busters*
6. **b.** Harper Lee
7. **a.** Charles Webb
8. **c.** *The Remains of the Day*
9. **b.** Tess of the D'Urbervilles

PAGE 156

Rest Break

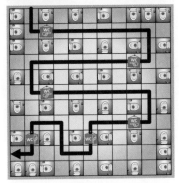

THREE-IN-ONE • CARDAMOM / CINNAMON / NUTMEG

Answers

PAGE 157

Film Quotes 2

S	N	I	F	F		C	H	A	S	E		R	P	M
G	A	T	O	R		O	I	L	E	D		A	R	E
T	H	E	L	I	O	N	K	I	N	G		T	I	S
			D	A	N	C	E		T	I	T	A	N	S
I	N	F	E	R	N	O			N	I	T	T	Y	
V	O	I	D		A	U	S		A	G	R	O		
A	N	N			R	I	T	A		E	U	R	O	
N	E	D	S		A	S	T	I	R		D	I	E	S
A	S	I	A		B	E	A	M		L	A	C		
		N	I	D	E		R	B	I		A	L	T	A
A	N	G	L	E			U	N	C	L	E	A	R	
S	E	N	S	E	S		A	R	R	A	Y			
H	I	E		M	O	N	S	T	E	R	S	I	N	C
E	L	M		E	R	A	T	O		E	S	S	A	Y
S	L	O		D	A	M	O	N		D	A	T	E	D

PAGE 158

Big-Nosed Bornean

C	O	S	T		P	A	V	E	S		G	L	I	B
U	T	A	H		A	L	I	V	E		R	A	R	A
L	A	V	E		S	E	D	E	R		A	R	A	B
P	R	O	B	O	S	C	I	S	M	O	N	K	E	Y
A	U	R	O	R	A			O	B	I				
			Y	O	G	I		O	N	E	T	I	M	E
L	E	S	S		E	N	O	L		A	E	S	O	P
E	A	U		O	S	T	R	I	C	H		E	L	I
A	R	M	O	R		R	A	V	E		B	R	A	C
F	L	O	R	I	D	A		E	L	I	E			
		L	E	R			E	R	R	A	T	A		
N	A	S	A	L	I	S	L	A	R	V	A	T	U	S
E	R	I	N		N	A	O	M	I		T	I	N	T
T	E	N	D		K	R	A	I	T		E	V	E	R
S	A	G	O		S	A	N	D	Y			S	E	R	A

PAGE 159

Sport Maze

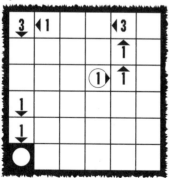

ONE LETTER LESS OR MORE •
UNDERWEAR

PAGE 160

Typist

P. For each word, the letter changes that comes first in the alphabet.

LETTER LINE • **SEMIQUAVER;**
MAUVE, SQUIRM, EAVES, REQUIEM, QUERIES

PAGE 161

Word Sudoku

UNCANNY TURN •
SNOWBOARDING

PAGE 162

Kakuro

SANDWICH • WOOD

PAGE 163

Themeless 6

S	P	A	M		T	H	I	E	F		P	A	L	E
L	E	N	A		H	O	R	D	E		R	A	I	N
I	N	T	E	R	E	S	T	E	D		O	R	E	O
M	A	R	S	H	E	S		N	E	R	V	O	U	S
S	L	A	T	E	D			R	U	I	N			
			R	A	G	S		H	A	N	D	B	A	G
A	M	M	O		E	T	H	Y	L		E	U	R	O
B	E	A			R	I	D			R	I	B		
C	O	R	K		M	A	C	R	O		P	R	A	Y
S	W	E	E	N	E	Y		A	R	E	A			
		S	T	O	L		A	C	R	O	S	S		
M	E	N	T	H	O	L		A	T	T	E	M	P	T
O	P	E	L		D	I	C	T	I	O	N	A	R	Y
L	E	S	E		I	D	O	T	O		T	H	I	N
L	E	T	S		C	S	P	A	N		S	A	G	E

PAGE 164

Sudoku Twin

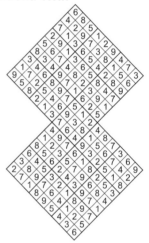

DELETE ONE • DELETE F AND FIND
LOTTERY WIN.

PAGE 165

In Balance

B. $A = B + C + D$, $C = B + D$,
$A = 3D$ so $3D = 2B + 2D$, $3D - 2D = 2B$ so $D = 2B$.

QUICK CROSSWORD •

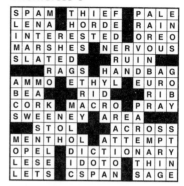

218

PAGE 166

From Acorn to Tree

M	I	S	T		D	U	E	L	S		S	A	N	D
A	N	T	A		I	N	D	I	E		O	T	O	E
S	C	O	R	N	S	C	O	R	E	S	C	O	P	E
S	A	P	P	O	R	O		A	T	T	I	M	E	S
		I	D	O				H	U	E				
H	O	T	T	U	B	S		R	E	D	T	A	P	E
A	G	O		L	E	A	S	E		A	R	I	A	
S	L	O	P	E	S	L	O	P	S	F	L	O	P	S
T	E	L	L		A	L	E	T	A		S	E	E	
A	S	S	E	R	T	S		L	A	R	G	E	S	S
		D	U	H		G	O	O						
A	P	O	G	E	E	S	D	E	F	U	N	C	T	
F	L	O	E	S	F	L	E	E	S	F	R	E	E	S
R	A	Z	E		T	U	T	E	E		D	A	D	A
O	N	E	S		S	M	A	R	T		S	T	E	R

PAGE 167

Zoo Logic

1. fauna—[C] animal life in a region. I studied up on Kenya's *fauna* so I'd know what to look for during the safari.

2. nicker—[C] whinny like a horse. Tex *nickers* so well that people feed him oats!

3. savanna—[A] grassland. The cheetah stalked its prey from the tall grass of the *savanna*.

4. nocturnal—[C] active at night. City dwellers joke that the *nocturnal* chirping of crickets is a more bothersome sound than the noise of late-night traffic.

5. vulpine—[B] like a fox. Rudy approached the deviled eggs with a *vulpine* lick of his chops.

6. flews—[C] droopy lips, like a bloodhound's. When my dog Fido snores, his *flews* flap in the breeze.

7. aquiline—[A] resembling an eagle's beak. Adrien Brody makes an *aquiline* nose look good.

8. piebald—[B] spotted. Of the many cattle breeds, I like the piebald Holsteins best.

9. headwater—[A] source of a stream. Lewis and Clark led the first expedition up the Missouri River to its *headwater*.

10. clutch—[B] nest of eggs. Debbie defends her dinner plate as aggressively as a hen protects her *clutch*.

11. tawny—[A] of a warm sandy color. My favorite thing about a lion cub is its *tawny* coat.

12. prehensile—[A] adapted for grasping. The giraffe's long tongue and *prehensile* upper lip help it strip leaves from the branches of treetops.

13. estivate—[C] sleep through the summer. Desert reptiles *estivate* underground to seek refuge from the strong sun.

14. territorial—[B] relating to a specific area. Cats are very *territorial* creatures; my dog has learned it's best to keep out of my kitty's preferred places to nap!

15. polecat—[C] skunk. Tina has invented a pungent perfume she ought to call *Polecat*.

VOCABULARY RATINGS

9 & below: Shaky legs
10–12: Making strides
13–15: Full gallop

PAGE 168

Dreams

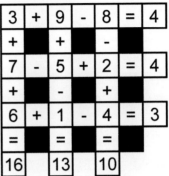

Dreaming is often compared to hallucinating; sometimes people can even fly in their dreams.

PAGE 169

Do the Math

3	+	9	−	8	=	4
+		+		−		
7	−	5	+	2	=	4
+		−		+		
6	+	1	−	4	=	3
=		=		=		
16		13		10		

DOUBLETALK • BEER/BIER

PAGE 170

Retronyms 1

M	A	R	I		A	A	R	O	N		T	S	A	R
A	L	E	C		C	R	O	W	E		I	N	C	A
S	I	L	E	N	T	F	I	L	M		S	A	R	I
S	A	I	L	O	R	S		S	E	S	S	I	O	N
E	S	C	A	P	E			S	A	U	L			
			N	E	S	S		C	I	N	E	M	A	S
L	E	W	D		S	P	A	R	S		S	A	L	T
A	S	H			A	A	A				I	L	A	
S	C	O	P		C	H	R	I	S		F	L	I	T
H	E	L	L	I	O	N		N	I	N	O			
			E	A	R	N		M	A	R	K	U	P	
T	O	M	C	A	T	S		A	P	P	E	A	S	E
E	L	I	A		E	Y	E	G	L	A	S	S	E	S
M	E	L	T		S	N	O	R	E		T	H	A	T
P	O	K	E		T	E	N	O	R		S	A	S	S

PAGE 171

Futoshiki

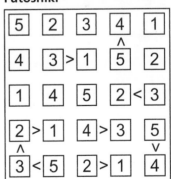

TRIANAGRAM • DETERS / RESTED

PAGE 172

Celebration

Letter W. The consonants are always composed of white, blue, red and yellow confetti.

QUICK WORD SEARCH •

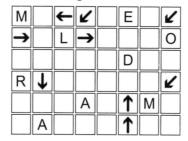

PAGE 173

Retronyms 2

PAGE 174

Figure 8's

1. **a.** Axel jump
2. **c.** Salchow
3. **a.** Dorothy Hamill
4. **b.** Bone
5. **c.** 1990
6. **b.** Music with vocals
7. **a.** Oslo, Norway
8. **b.** They were killed in a plane crash
9. **a.** East Germany

PAGE 175

Find the Right Word

MELODRAMA

CHANGELINGS • BARBERSHOP / ROCKABILLY / ORCHESTRAL

PAGE 176

Sudoku

6	3	4	8	7	9	1	2	5
8	5	1	2	4	3	7	9	6
7	2	9	1	6	5	3	8	4
2	4	3	5	9	8	6	1	7
1	9	6	7	3	2	4	5	8
5	7	8	6	1	4	9	3	2
3	1	5	4	8	7	2	6	9
4	6	2	9	5	1	8	7	3
9	8	7	3	2	6	5	4	1

SYMBOL SUMS •
$12 - 8 \times 13 \div 4 = 13$

PAGE 177

Graffiti

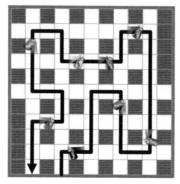

FRIENDS • THEY ARE ALL ENGLISH WORDS OF DUTCH ORIGIN.

PAGE 178

Dynamic Duos

PAGE 179

Word Ladders

laser, large, learn, later, table, beast, beams

water, waste, swear, laser, flare, false, falls

PAGE 180

Shapely

Shape 2. In each column, place the three squares on top of each other. If each of the small squares on top of each other has a different color then you get a black square at the bottom, otherwise it is white.

DOODLE PUZZLE • CasualTy

PAGE 181

Freshen Up

PAGE 182

Language Quirks 1

S	P	A	S		S	P	E	A	R		B	O	A	S
K	U	R	T		P	E	R	L	E		E	R	L	E
U	S	E	E		A	R	S	O	N		F	R	E	E
A	H	A	R	D	N	U	T	T	O	C	R	A	C	K
			N	O	G				I	I	I			
S	C	H	O	O	L	S		A	R	T	E	M	I	S
I	L	A		M	E	L	O	N		E	N	O	L	A
L	A	S	S		D	O	O	N	E		D	R	O	P
A	S	T	E	R		T	H	E	S	E		E	N	O
S	P	A	N	I	S	H		S	T	E	L	L	A	R
			T	C	U				I	R	E			
S	P	U	R	O	F	T	H	E	M	O	M	E	N	T
T	O	N	I		F	A	U	N	A		M	I	C	E
A	R	T	E		E	R	G	O	T		O	N	A	N
T	K	O	S		R	E	E	S	E		N	E	A	T

PAGE 183

Umbrella Trouble

X = 31. Start at the lowest number (6) and work clockwise, adding progressive odd numbers each time and jumping two segments at a time to unravel the sequence: 6 (+ 1) 7 (+ 3) 10 (+ 5) 15 (+ 7) 22 (+ 9) 31 (+ 11) 42.

LETTER LINE • ASSOCIATION; OASIS, COINS, CASINO, ACTION, COAST

PAGE 184

Sport Maze

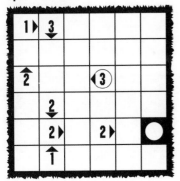

ONE LETTER LESS OR MORE • NIGHTMARE

PAGE 185

Magic

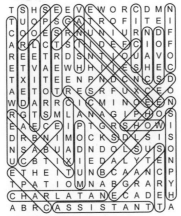

The word most often used when performing magic tricks is undoubtedly the incantation "Abracadabra."

PAGE 186

Language Quirks 2

B	R	A	Y		E	R	I	E	S		F	R	O	M
L	O	L	A		L	U	R	C	H		R	E	D	O
A	M	E	N		D	E	A	R	E		E	N	I	D
B	A	C	K	T	O	S	Q	U	A	R	E	O	N	E
			E	A	R			R	U	B				
A	R	S	E	N	A	L		T	S	H	I	R	T	S
L	I	T		A	D	L	E	R		R	E	E	S	E
I	C	E	T		O	A	S	E	S		S	E	A	N
A	C	R	E	S		M	A	V	I	S		D	R	S
S	I	N	A	T	R	A		I	M	P	A	S	S	E
			L	I	I			M	C	C				
U	N	D	E	R	T	H	E	W	E	A	T	H	E	R
T	O	R	O		T	A	P	I	R		O	O	Z	E
E	L	O	N		E	M	I	L	E		R	B	I	S
P	O	P	I		R	A	C	E	D		S	O	O	T

PAGE 187

Word Sudoku

UNCANNY TURN • RED SKY IN THE MORNING

PAGE 188

Cage the Animals

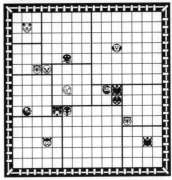

FRIENDS • EACH CAN HAVE THE PREFIX PAN- TO FORM A NEW WORD.

PAGE 189

Who Said That?

1. Winston Churchill
2. Eleanor Roosevelt
3. Gen. Douglas MacArthur
4. Emperor Hirohito
5. Gen. George S. Patton
6. FDR
7. Anne Frank
8. Rosie the Riveter

Answers

PAGE 190

Themeless 7

F	I	N	D		B	A	N	G	S		O	C	H	O
A	D	E	E		O	B	E	L	I		C	H	O	P
D	O	W	N	G	R	A	D	E	S		A	A	R	E
E	N	E	M	I	E	S			E	T	E	R	N	A	L
S	T	R	A	N	D			E	D	I	T			
			R	O	O	M		U	R	A	N	I	U	M
H	A	C	K		M	I	L	L	S		A	L	L	A
A	L	L			E	S	T				L	A	D	
R	O	A	R		I	N	U	R	E		B	Y	R	D
M	U	S	E	U	M	S		A	X	L	E			
		S	L	A	P			P	I	E	R	R	E	
C	A	M	E	R	A	S		O	R	A	T	I	O	N
E	V	A	N		S	U	T	H	E	R	L	A	N	D
L	E	T	T		S	E	A	R	S		E	N	D	O
T	R	E	S		E	D	G	E	S		S	T	O	W

PAGE 191

Beady

Color 5. The beads are split in groups of three. The color of the middle bead is a combination of the outer two colors.

BLOCK ANAGRAM • FLOODING

PAGE 192-193

Piggy Bank Puzzles
1.

2.

PAGE 194

Word Pyramid

(1) FA
(2) FAR
(3) RAFT
(4) AFTER
(5) FASTER
(6) FRETSAW
(7) SOFTWARE

PAGE 195

Governing Bodies

1. **a.** Athens
2. **c.** Russia
3. **a.** England in the 1600s, under Charles I and Cromwell
4. **a.** Iceland—its Althing
5. **c.** Fidel Castro of Cuba
6. **a.** England and Portugal
7. **a.** Tonga
8. **b.** United States
9. **b.** The European Commission

PAGE 196

Hourglass

(1) EXPULSE
(2) PLEXUS
(3) PULSE
(4) PLUS
(5) SPUR
(6) SIRUP
(7) PURISM
(8) UMPIRES

PAGE 197

Christmas Carols

E	X	A	M		C	A	L	I		A	O	L
K	I	V	A		O	X	E	N		G	T	O
E	V	E	N		M	I	D	N	I	G	H	T
			G	U	M	S		A	D	I	E	U
T	E	R	E	S	A		S	T	E	E	R	S
A	M	O	R	E		P	L	E	A			
B	O	Y		W	A	Y			J	O	Y	
			F	A	I	R		F	J	O	R	D
G	I	V	I	N	G		T	R	I	B	E	S
A	S	E	A	T		P	A	I	N			
F	A	I	T	H	F	U	L		G	N	A	T
F	I	N		E	A	R	L		L	O	B	E
E	D	S		M	A	R	Y		E	D	E	N

PAGE 198

Play Ball

C	A	N	D	L	E	S	T	I	C	K	P	A	R	K
O		I		E		H		F		I		N		I
M	E	M	O	R	I	A	L		D	W	I	G	H	T
I		O		O		R		G		I		E		
S	P	Y		Y	A	K		I	N		A	L	E	C
K			V			S		J		C		F		H
E	B	B	E	T	S		P	O	L	O		O	D	E
Y		U	N	I		P	R	E		U		O		E
	W	R	I	G	L	E	Y		A	N	O	D	E	S
F		G		E		G		B	I	T				E
E	V	E		R	A	G	G	E	D	Y	A	N	N	
N		R			Y		R			R	O	B		
W	E	B	B	E	R		A	L	C	A	T	R	A	Z
A		U		Y	U	M		I		S		M		I
Y	A	N	K	E	E		O	N	E	H	E	A	R	T

Good Sport

1. aficionado—[C] buff. A nascent fishing *aficionado*, Jonathan insists on using spinning lures instead of worms as bait.

2. wheelhouse—[A] batter's ideal swinging range. To his chagrin, the pitcher threw into the slugger's *wheelhouse* and cost his team a run.

3. laugher—[B] lopsided win. Even though the game was a *laugher*, the victors graciously greeted the losing team.

4. gambit—[A] opening maneuver. That sneaky *gambit* might earn you a four-move checkmate, but it will cost you willing opponents.

5. arbitrate—[B] serve as umpire. When an argument broke out over the team's last cupcake, a coach stepped in to *arbitrate*.

6. chaff—[A] tease. Chloe *chaffs* Alex each time she beats him at badminton.

7. thimblerig—[B] con game. Tom thought he could outsmart the *thimblerig,* but he lost his temper and $5.

8. see—[A] match, as a poker bet. I'll *see* your pie bet with some ice cream.

9. ludic—[B] playful. Fans of the Harlem Globetrotters enjoy their *ludic* antics on the basketball court.

10. baize—[A] pool-table fabric. Eddie is such a billiards fanatic that his man cave is carpeted in *baize*.

11. maffick—[A] celebrate joyfully. The team *mafficked* its victory by rushing the field.

12. cat's game—[A] tie in tic-tac-toe. It took a hasty, careless move to break the longstanding series of *cat's games.*

13. token—[C] game piece. My family plays Parcheesi with buttons because the official *tokens* were lost long ago.

14. ruff—[B] play a trump card. I smiled at her taunts, knowing I would *ruff* on the next hand.

15. hat trick—[B] three hockey goals by one player. After Gretzky's *hat trick*, the ice was littered with fans' caps.

VOCABULARY RATINGS

9 & below: Dark horse
10–12: Contender
13–15: Champion

Answers

CREDITS

Cover photo credit:
ziviani/Shutterstock

Puzzle Credits:
Sam Bellotto Jr.: 107, 126, 133, 181
Emily Cox & Henry Rathvon: 15, 62, 115, 167, 199
Peter Frank: Binairo, Cage the Animals, Concentration, Find the Right Word, Futoshiki, Horoscope, Hourglass, Kakuro, Keep Going, Letter Soup, Number Cluster, Sport Maze, Spot the Differences, Sudoku, Sudoku Twin, Sudoku X, Word Parts, Word Search, Word Sudoku, Word Wheel
Maggie Ellis: 78
Frank Gehry: 148-149
Jean Griffing: 12, 37
Linda Lather: 20, 134
Don Law: 56, 144
Mary Leonard: 140, 163, 190
Teresa Lucchetti: 28, 64, 129
Myles Mellor: 143, 178, 198, 178, 198
Brian O'Shea: 47
Peggy O'Shea: 100
Karen Peterson: 31, 40, 84, 97
Puzzlemakers: 192-193
Ken Russell and Philip Carter: 42, 77, 112-113, 183
John M. Samson: 17, 34, 55, 60, 75, 80, 87, 91, 94, 114, 119, 147, 152, 157, 166, 170, 173
Michele Sayer: 8, 69, 72
Justin Scroggie: 13
Debra Steilen: 52, 120, 189
Tim Wagner: 123, 182, 186
Cindy Wheeler: 23, 50, 158
Kelly Whitt: 44, 104, 197

• Puzzles unless noted above: BrainSnack®
• RD-owned unless noted above:
  Sudoku: 21, 145
  Trivia Quiz: 11, 25, 46, 67, 88, 108, 111, 130, 155, 174, 195